A SYLLABUS

OF

STAGE LIGHTING

BY

STANLEY McCANDLESS

CONTENTS

CONTENTS

FOREWORD

In this the eleventh edition of the Syllabus, revisions recognize recent developments. In particular the entire third chapter on Control has been rewritten by John Hood an associate in the Yale Drama School laboratory of George Izenour, a pioneer in electronic control. Harvey Smith, the writer's associate for the last few years, has checked the figures suggested for various stages in the allotments of budget for equipment in Chapter Four and other subsequent sections.

The outline form of the preceeding editions is maintained and filled out for easier reading. Inasmuch as the Syllabus is intended for teaching, it is believed that the visual form of heading, subheading and numbered or lettered paragraphs shows most clearly the relative importance and association of the various ideas, types of equipment and uses they are intended for. Illustrative material in the form of lantern slides and film strips of pertinent material including new developments as they come along should accompany lectures based on the Syllabus. Problems and questions, laboratory work with equipment demonstrating its use, crew work on actual productions and demonstrations of theory or the pursuit of projects suggested by these pages will fill out a course in lighting which the Syllabus can only start and serve as a brief text.

Light is the means of all seeing, yet the rays themselves are invisible. Only under special conditions as with a searchlight is it possible to see the density, color, and direction of the rays and even here no indication of the movement of the speed of light from the source to a distant point is given. This makes the design and control of light a kind of magic which must be mastered as well as any technique of expression. Most of the characteristics of light and seeing have been known for many years but the electric lamp has provided such an extended scope of expression that many have come to think of lighting as a field of electrical engineering. Actually, lighting as it benefits man is an ancient art which we are now able to express more freely through electricity.

Stage lighting is designed to serve with the other elements of production in creating a dramatic visual effect and when it enhances the illusion of the play, it most nearly approaches the ultimate in its use. The many demonstrations of artificial lighting seem to indicate that lighting may be something of an art in itself. It is a mistake to consider lighting solely as a source of illumination for static visual expressions — painting, sculpture, and architecture. It has the vital characteristic of music and poetry — movement. It embodies some of the elements of expression of each of the fine arts and the designer who makes the plans, as well as the operator who manipulates the control board, must have the ability to evaluate these elements.

When the artist, through a mastery of the intricacies of technique, undertakes any problem of lighting, his expression, be it part of theatrical production, painting, sculpture, or architecture, is a visual entity — a direct application of a vital means whereby man gains pleasure and emotion through the eye.

New Haven
Sept. 1964

A SYLLABUS OF STAGE LIGHTING

By

STANLEY McCANDLESS
Professor of Lighting
The Department of Drama—School of Fine Arts
Yale University

The modern stage has as its aid a magician—Light, Electric Light. Any skilled producer today must think in its terms, work with and by it. It threads its way through all the conditions of producing plays. Both scenery and costume must consider it at every moment. It goes far in creating and maintaining atmosphere. It can also do much to create and maintain the mood in which the play is to be received; can do much in preparing for a big scene; can do an equal amount in heightening its value. We are indeed just at the beginning in understanding its possibilities. Just how far, for instance, lighting may go in suggesting special characteristics, in representing certain types of character, is still a matter of experiment. We have, then, already learned that lighting in stagecraft is fundamental and may be revelatory. The extent to which it may itself be creative, we have still fully to learn.

Geo. P. Baker.

New Haven, Conn.
September, 1931.

1 9 6 4

INTRODUCTION

The design and control of light may deal with natural illumination, but generally, lighting involves the creation and regulation of visual effects produced by artificial sources. Since the invention of the electric lamp, the conquest over darkness has been extended and a new medium of expression is available. A great deal of man's pleasure in beauty is due to the sense of vision through light. It is older than man, but it is difficult after so many centuries of primitive methods of extending the waking hours when darkness falls, to be fully aware of the possibilities that are now at hand.

Light as it appeals to the individual seems to be accepted as one of the mysteries of nature. The scientist has solved many of the age-old secrets and put them to use in the service of mankind; but the manner in which light appeals to the individual still offers many challenging aspects for investigation.

The designer has available the techniques and equipment developed by the engineer, but he often feels hindered by the technical limitations involved. The engineer slights the appeal to the individual because it is not always reducible to scientific procedure and the designer chafes at the technical limitations because they seem to prohibit any flexibility of interpretation. Both individuals have the common goal of wishing to make light useful. Lighting needs to be defined so that its functions are understood. Then the engineer and designer, each in his own way, can strive to satisfy the need for a more scientific and artistic use of artificial light.

In a particular field—the theatre—the demand for an extensive use of artificial light was created when a roof was put over the stage and auditorium. Light has played an important part in the theatre ever since its inception, because life seems inseparable from it, and before the theatre went indoors, light in its various naturalistic aspects was considered as one of the great mysteries. To some degree this concept of light still rests on that high plane. Fortunately in the theatre today there is a definite attempt to study these mysteries of lighting and to use them in relation to human life.

There is a great gulf between such a conception and that which motivates the average use of artificial illumination. Something spiritual was lost in the step from the courtyard, where the use of symbols forced the imagination to supply the lack of lighting "effects", to the indoor theatre where the practical need for visibility required the use of artificial illumination. The coming of electricity and the incandescent lamp caused a revolution in the theatre. The centuries of darkness were gone. Light in vast quantities was poured on the stage—everywhere, indiscriminately—to give more and more illumination. In this respect we may have lost more than we have gained.

But there were many advantages in the transition from outdoors to the theatre under a roof. If it rained or got dark, still the show could go on. Furthermore, in addition to artificial light's giving visibility, it could be controlled and even colored to simulate, however crudely, the broad effects of dawn and sunset, day and night. The results were ineffectual, so that although light served a new function—that of giving the effect of naturalism—there was little effort to use light for this purpose until it could be had in greater quantities and put under better control.

The swing to realism in the theatre at the end of the last century found electric illumination still something of a novelty. The control apparatus was expensive and few people knew enough about its characteristics to achieve naturalistic results. However, the trend started a definite movement to use light to give a semblance of time and place. Elaborate mechanisms were developed to simulate the effects of light in nature. The electric lamp provided a great stimulation to the use of effects—magic lantern slides of all kinds imitating clouds, lightning, moving scenery, rippling water, and so on. The greater quantities of light available permitted a more extensive use of color and the representation of sunsets, sunrises, moonlight, held audiences spellbound. But these first uses of the electric lamp did not really simulate the effects of nature convincingly. It had to depend upon the appeal of novelty and the audience's acceptance of broad suggestion. It seemed a marvelous achievement over the limitation of the past, but it did not create a complete illusion. It did prove, however, that light in nature was something more than a means to visibility.

Richard Wagner may have suggested the possibilities inherent in the use of light, together with the other mechanical contrivances that his operas have since developed for the theatre, but it was such men as Appia and Craig, who first saw something more in the dramatic contribution of background

1

to the stage than had the archrealists. They saw that through the use of light a more definite composition, based on an artistic harmony of the visible elements of the stage, could be created. They pointed the way to a more dramatic conception of scenery and the design of the space through which the actor moved. The actor, a three-dimensional object, deserved a harmonious plasticity of background. If the scenery was to be solid, the old systems giving general illumination by means of border lights, wing lights, and footlights, had to be replaced by equipment which would give carefully modeled distribution. This new function of lighting was made possible by the increasing flexibility of electrical control of light. Composition became another function of lighting and perhaps the keynote of the modern theatre movement.

Plastic composition was only a means to an end in Appia's theory. Unless light can increase mystery and illusion, it contributes little. The changes of light in nature, although we know them intimately, never cease to make us wonder. Whether we try to simulate the effects of nature by artificial light or to treat it arbitrarily for the sake of dramatic effect as an integral part of the play, light supplies a mood quality that almost escapes tangible analysis.

This property of lighting which springs from the psychological, emotional effects of vision, must wait on the results of more complete research and tradition. The dramatist may know them by instinct and suggest the associational, visual, dramatic qualities of such situations as sunset, moonlight, etc., in his manuscript. In varying degrees he learns to rely on light to increase the mood in the play. Insofar as light creates an unconscious illusion harmonious with the spirit of the play, and increases the dramatic nature of each situation within the various scenes, it serves its ultimate function in connection with the audience. The atmosphere or mood light gives to any visual sensation is witness of this fourth function.

I. DEFINITION

Stage Lighting may be defined as the use of light to create a sense of visibility, naturalism, composition, and mood. This is a loose definition and probably not clear until the terms have been explained. Furthermore, while the order of consideration of the functions is more or less fixed, they overlap, and as time goes on, when realism loses its hold on the playwright, naturalism may be completely absorbed in composition and mood. Perhaps the latter should even now be called atmosphere and some attention should be paid to the great drive in the world outside the theatre to promote the use of light to give comfort. The lineup of the functions of lighting in this case would be visibility, comfort, composition, and atmosphere. With these in mind it is possible for the artist and the technician to work toward a common goal and it provides the student and even the layman with a basis for criticism and a guide in the development of taste for good lighting.

II. FUNCTIONS

The objective of any lighting scheme is to achieve a coordinated application of these functions. Basically they represent the degree of usefulness of lighting to the individual in the theatre in terms of mental or psychological reaction.

The ultimate success of any lighting scheme depends upon the degree of penetration of the inner consciousness of the observer through his sense of sight. Thus, although the approach is through the eye, the result depends upon the awakening of the imagination and intellectual processes.

A. VISIBILITY

This covers the range from threshold sensitivity to extreme sharpness of vision (acuity). By its very nature, artificial light can be controlled to provide distinct vision of essential details such as the actor's face, or it can leave obscure objects and surfaces which are of secondary importance. Often the imagination is awakened more completely by the mere suggestion of dimly lighted forms. The director, believing that the actor is the most effective means of conveying emotion to the audience, is primarily interested in visibility.

B. NATURALISM

An audience unconsciously tries to orient itself with relation to the stage picture and tends to accept the lighting in terms of naturalistic or motivating sources. Thus, naturalism covers

2

the approach which extends from utter abstraction through stylized arbitrary effects to the simulation of naturalistic lighting in terms of utter realism. Realistic plays depend upon motivation (actual places at certain times) whereas abstract situations, such as review numbers, are arbitrary and as such demand practically no indication of time and place. In view of the above, the playwright and the designer are often most concerned with this particular function, the latter many times at the expense of visibility, which is required on the acting area.

C. COMPOSITION

The pictorial aspect of the stage is under the almost absolute control of the designer. The style of the production as indicated by the playwright and chosen by the producer or director, determines the approach for the designer. Artificial light should be designed and controlled within its characteristics just as definitely as the scenery, properties, and costumes. To some degree the grouping of the actors also comes under the head of pictorial effect. When the designer determines the relative see-ability of the various portions of the stage, he is determining the arrangement of brightnesses, colors, and forms in terms of the best principles of dramatic composition, and he may even go beyond the field of expression of painting, sculpture, and architecture into the field of music by determining a sequence of picturizations and rhythms of dramatic movement.

D. MOOD

In the process of working out the other functions of lighting, the atmosphere or feeling created by the visual effect must be kept in mind. In fact it is possible that this function is primary. If it is properly expressed, the other three will be right also. However this function is the most abstract and most closely allied to the idea indicated by the playwright and desired by the audience so that it can be considered separately from the other functions. Basically it is achieved only in terms of the fundamental psychological reactions of the audience.

III. QUALITIES

Inasmuch as the approach to the mind of the individual in terms of vision is through the eye, its physiological characteristics serve as a guide in the design of any lighting. Further, these qualities indicate the extent of control of the patterns of light radiation that should be provided in order to give a full range of sensory visual experience. Beyond this, even, they determine the usefulness of instruments, backgrounds, and control apparatus in terms of their ability to provide the visual components (intensity, color, form, and movement) of a series of effects.

A. INTENSITY OR BRIGHTNESS

The amount of visual radiation which enters the eye to give a sense of brightness from threshold to saturation, is comprised under this heading. The pupil opening actually determines the amount of light that reaches the eye (1-16 times) but simultaneous contrasts create the most noticeable effects of brightness range.

B. COLOR

The range of color sensitivity is included in the entire gamut of recognizable hues, tints, and shades, or expressed another way, the range of color, purity, and brightness discrimination, separately and collectively, which the eye is capable of recognizing. Some authorities indicate that this runs into several hundred thousands of steps.

C. FORM

One of the chief characteristics of the eye is the ability to recognize size, shape and position. Patterns of light radiation are recognized in the eye in terms of brightness and color differences.

D. MOVEMENT

Changes in any of the foregoing qualities are recognizable by the eye within definite limits of time, and they lend vitality and life to otherwise static pictures.

IV. METHODS*

Just as the process of playwriting and directing involves a heightening of the normal situation, giving it what we call a dramatic or theatrical emphasis, so must lighting be conceived in the same terms. It is a highly selective process, not only because the theatre is supposed to create glamour, emotion, and illusion, but because the technical and practical means of creating these effects are definitely limited.

The complexity of the problem of producing a play creates utter confusion until some reasonable method is established. The importance of each function of lighting varies in the mind of every worker in the theatre and with each style of production. These differences of point of view starting with the director, actor, designer, technician, and continuing even to the individuals of the audience, provide a practical problem of coordination. It is hoped that with a clear definition of each function much of this confusion will be eliminated and that a coordinated scheme for the production may result.

Once the artistic approach has been decided upon, then the practical problem of designing the visual effects which include scenery, costumes, properties, and technical features can proceed. The following methods of lighting the stage, related to the available equipment and standard methods of production is presented as a practical procedure.

Its importance lies far more in the principles indicated than in any of the details. Namely, in order to provide visibility on the acting area separate from the other parts of the stage picture, also to achieve the proper degree of flexibility, six areas are indicated for the average stage, but there is no reason why a small stage, an irregularly formed stage, or even a circus platform might not be divided into a suitable number of areas and be lighted on the same plan. The designer should use the following details only in so far as they apply directly to the problem. They are indicated more as examples for a normal setup and they should be departed from in case of any irregularity or any unusual condition.

A definite method promotes coordination and an efficient use of time and equipment. It even tends to establish a standard layout of instruments and control apparatus; a minimum for a budget which has the authority of precision beyond individual opinion. If the method is applied with reason these assets far exceed its limitations. See Appendix V.

A. ACTING AREA

In order to provide utter freedom of movement for the actor, the acting area should be lighted separately from the other portions of the stage. This will also guarantee proper visibility and accents in terms of composition. However, it is an utterly arbitrary process and must be handled very subtlely.

The average stage can be divided into six areas. Each should be lighted diagonally from the front to give a flexibility of brightness or color to various portions of the stage, to conform to the normal localized distribution of a spotlight; and to give the proper degree plasticity on the actor's face without causing distracting shadows to fall on the setting. Each area should be lighted by two instruments—generally spotlights.

The spotlights should be mounted and directed so that the angles of throw lie more or less consistently along the diagonal of the cube. Each of these twelve spotlights should be soft-edged to the extent that the areas blend together, but not so much that they cause undue spill of light

---

* See "A METHOD OF LIGHTING THE STAGE" Theatre Arts Books, Inc., N.Y. for a more complete, illustrated treatment by the author.

on the walls of the auditorium or on the upper parts of the setting.

Tints of color should be used both for the sake of efficiency and because nothing is highly visible under a strong color. Warm colors can be directed from the left, cool colors from the right, or vice versa. This provides light on the actor's face whether he turns right or left, maintains as much plasticity as possible, and gives a consistent direction to a motivating color.

To this end it is generally necessary to shape the beam so that it will be confined to the proper area. Each instrument should be connected through a dimmer so that the differences in distance of throw and density of color medium can be offset and also to provide a flexibility of brightness control within each area. Where the number of dimmers is limited, the spotlights may be ganged together, all the front left on one dimmer, the front right on another, the bridge left on a third, and the bridge right on the fourth.

B. BLENDING AND TONING

The border lights which should be hung so that they give an even illumination to the scenes of the set, are used primarily to blend the acting areas together and to give them a tone of color. The footlights are directed to tone the ceiling and the walls of the setting primarily, and also to eliminate, to a small degree, the shadows from the overhead lighting on the actor's face.

Both instruments need to contain much less wattage than previously in view of the fact that the settings should be less illuminated than the acting area. Each should be equipped with three color circuits, generally red, green and blue, controlled separately by dimmers. With these primary colors it is possible to attain almost any recognizable tint or shade in the spectrum.

The border lights or X-rays can use lighter tints of color because seldom is it necessary to provide strong color tonality from this source. They should be of such length and so directed that they illuminate the lower portion of the setting and acting area evenly.

Footlights have a tendency to cast shadows on the setting and are often only used to light the curtain when it is down. They should never be more than three quarters the width of the procenium and should be used sparingly.

C. BACKGROUND

Although the flats of a box set usually comprise the immediate background, the cyclorama, backings, entrances, and groundrows, seen through windows or doors in the box set, or visible in an exterior scene, come under the heading of background.

1. Cyclorama or backdrop. Overhead lights in one, two, or three colors are used to provide an even illumination of high intensity over the entire area. These units should be mounted well downstage from the cyclorama in the fly space so that the normal graded wash of light from the instruments available will eliminate wrinkles and not leave a horizontal dark band across the center of the cyclorama.

   Horizon lights (cyc foots) in three or four colors sometimes controlled in sections should project light upward from a close position, such as a cyc pit sunk in the floor, to give the effect of sunset or variation of color on the lower portions of the cyclorama.

2. Entrance and window backings. These should be illuminated softly by floodlights or backing strips so that the openings do not appear as a black void. The entrance units should be so arranged that the actor will cause little or no shadow as he makes his entrance. The window backings should be lighted like a small section of the cyclorama or backdrop.

3. Groundrows. These are pieces of scenery which are used to represent distant landscape or merely to serve as abstract masking pieces to hide the floor of the stage at the rear. They may be lighted from the front by one-, two-, or three-color strips so mounted that they do not cause a shadow on the backdrop. Often the groundrows will receive enough illumination from the cyclorama overheads so that the groundrow strips do not need to be used.

D. SPECIAL UNITS

Those units used to create special distributions of light beyond the illumination provided by the three groups above come under the heading of special instruments. Generally speaking they are used for motivation and accent purposes.

1. <u>Entrance and acting area specials.</u> Spotlights can be directed and matted to cover entrances and special pieces of furniture or objects for the sake of visibility or accent in the composition. They are particularly necessary where the acting area lights do not cover sufficiently, and they should be of sufficient brightness to give an accent over the illumination already provided by the acting area lights.

2. <u>Sunlight.</u> Instruments producing almost parallel lines of light of high intensity which can be mounted well offstage to give the proper direction and distribution of light, generally through a window or doorway. They can often serve as acting area lights.

3. <u>Moonlight.</u> Similar to the instruments used for sunlight except for color and brightness. The color is generally light steel blue and the brightness greater than moonlight would be normally.

4. <u>Side lights, chandeliers, wall brackets, and fireplaces</u> are often used for motivating purposes. They should be dimmer than natural in order to cut down contrast glare, but if the side toward the audience is shielded, they may produce an illumination greater than they are expected to give.

5. <u>Special effects.</u> The effect machine and the Linnebach Lantern mounted on the bridge, in the wings, on the floor, or behind a translucent screen may be used to produce precise or general patterns in place of painted scenery. The effect machine is also useful for providing rain or snow or lighting in movement. Photoluminescent effects (by flourescence or phosphorescence) are used occasionally for decorative or ghostly scenes.

6

PART ONE

APPARATUS

It seems particularly true in the development of lighting that as science progresses through research, the equipment used is either borrowed from some antecedent phase or adopted wholly or in part for some use other than that for which it was originally designed. We have progressed from the candle era through gas to the electric lamp, yet we still see electric light fixtures designed to look as much like candles and oil lamps as possible. This practice applies even in the development of more technical equipment. The diversified demands made of lighting are still met with instruments and practices which do not apply sound scientific principles.

Methods of lighting should always be based on the characteristics of the available means of expression, and the most economical use of effort and equipment, a primary requisite in any work of art, can only be expressed when the artist has a complete mastery of the means at hand. There will have to be a general reconsideration of the relative importance of the various means of expression in producing a play before the expensive, yet limited, lighting apparatus of today can be used effectively and with the greatest economy. A wagon load of bricks and lumber can only build a house of a certain size, but in the hands of the expert artist it will be a good house—both useful and beautiful.

An expert who knows his profession can put to telling use almost any equipment. Yet his capabilities are undoubtedly increased with the right materials and instruments. The expensive and flexible layouts such as we often see today are not apt to fulfill their purpose, even when used by an expert. Stage lighting equipment and switchboards seem medieval in comparison with electrical control and equipment developed for purposes outside the theatre. Unless the design of the layout of equipment is made in accordance with an understanding of the purpose it is to serve, economic and artistic waste will result. Too few theatre people are able to express their technical needs precisely enough for the manufacturer and the engineer to give them what they need.

1. LIGHT SOURCES*

Light sources give out visible radiation which is usually produced by the incandescence of a tungsten filament. However, there is more and more reason to consider the arc, and the gaseous vapor tube.

The transformation of electrical energy into incandescent radiation is the operating principle of most practical light sources used today. With the increase in the temperature of the radiator, there is a change in wave length. As the wave lengths of radiation reach the visible range from the infra-red zone, red, orange, yellow, through blue, are added to make white. The convection of the air currents surrounding the radiator (tungsten filament in a bulb) and the dissipation of heat by conduction tend to carry off most of the energy in the form of heat and to reduce the efficiency factor (the light output to the power input). Thus the relative efficiency of the available tungsten sources is low (somewhere between 3 and 10 per cent). The flourescent sources are two to three times this amount.

The incandescent lamp is the most easily controlled, and thus the most used on the stage. The arc source, with the higher efficiency and whiter light, is used only for special effects and for long throws. The gaseous sources, of which the mercury, sodium, and flourescent types are examples, are being more widely used every day, and as a result sources which promise to be from four to six times as efficient as the incandescent lamp are being developed. At present they are expensive, require auxiliary apparatus to operate them and are not easily controlled for use on the stage, but they promise to be the most direct means for producing a definite color in the form of a line of light.

I. HISTORY

The development of lighting in the indoor theatre depended primarily upon the available light sources, from the candle down through the oil lamp and gas jet to the incandescent lamp. There were other sources, such as the limelight and the arc, developed in the last century which had considerable in-

---

* An excellent reference for a complete discussion of the electric lamp can be found in the General Electric Lamp Bulletin.

fluence in extending the producer's conception of the functions of light in the theatre. But today our interest is primarily in the incandescent tungsten filament lamp and the newer gaseous tube.

A. THE FIRST INCANDESCENT LAMP

Edison in this country and Swan in England produced almost simultaneously a practical form of incandescent lamp in 1879. The filament was a carbonized bamboo fiber and probably gave off about 4 lumens per watt. This filament was mounted in the glass bulb from which the air had been exhausted to prevent rapid oxidation.

B. THE TUNGSTEN FILAMENT

About 1907 the first tungsten-filament lamp was made. This more than doubled the efficiency of the output, and the terminology switched from candle power to watts as an indication of light output capacity.

C. GAS FILLED LAMPS

About 1913 it was found that the introduction of a combination of nitrogen and argon gas would slow up convection and oxidation and thus permit the filament to be burned at a higher temperature for a longer period of time. This became known as the type-C lamp in contradistinction to the vacuum lamp which became type B. Again the efficiency of output was stepped up over twice, to as many as twenty-two lumens per watt.

Up to this time the largest lamp that could be produced was the 100-candle power size. This burned approximately as much current as our present 100-watt size, but gave off less than a quarter of the amount of light. Larger lamps soon became available up to 1,000 watts in size.

D. VARIED FORMS

Rapid advances have been made in all forms of lamps, which are familiar to all. The motion-picture industry has created a tremendous demand for high-powered incandescent lamps in the making of sound pictures. As a result, the 5,000 and 10,000 watt G-type lamps have become standard products. Reflector lamps in many sizes are the most recent development.

There are today over many thousand different forms of lamps, but the following outline will concern itself primarily only with those which are generally useful in stage lighting.

E. THE GASEOUS CONDUCTOR SOURCES

The future seems to point to an extended use of luminous gaseous sources. The principle has been developed to include the efficient mercury lamp; the sodium lamp with the characteristic yellow color, such as is often seen in use of lighting highways today, and flourescent tubes which can be made to glow brilliantly in a wide range of colors by using the invisible ultra-violet rays given off from a mercury arc.

F. ARCS

Carbon arcs still have use in follow spots, as UV sources and in effect machines. Xenon arcs are used to some extent in the European theatre.

G. AIMS

There is a need for a brilliant, white, point-source of light for use in optical equipment, and a line of light of a definite color for use in strip lighting. The more these sources can approach the efficiency of cold light, the greater will be the use of light for artistic purposes, because of the greater freedom of control which will be provided.

II. THE INCANDESCENT LAMP*

A tungsten filament has a very high melting point. It will not evaporate unduly at a temperature just below that point. Evaporation causes blackening of the glass bulb, surrounding the filament. Tungsten offers high resistance to the flow of electric current.

A. ELECTRICAL CONSIDERATIONS**

$W=VA$

Any material such as tungsten which offers a resistance (ohms) to the flow of current (amperes) will absorb the pressure (volts) which is applied to it, and the energy or power involved will be converted into heat. If pressure is applied in the form of voltage, current can be forced through the resistance in proportional amounts, and the heat becomes greater and greater until the body begins to glow and give off light. The power (watts) consumed is the product of the voltage times the amperage, and where the voltage is normally constant (110, 115, 120) the amperes are proportional to the wattage.

$$R = K\frac{Length}{Area}$$

Resistance is directly proportional to the conductivity constant of the material at various temperatures (tungsten becomes greater under heat, carbon becomes less) times the length of the conductor, and inversely proportional to its cross section. Obviously, from this, a tungsten wire which is to be made to work as a light source of certain brightness should not be heated up beyond its normal capacity (to stay in solid form), and at the same time, it should be able to utilize all the pressure or voltage, so that the flow of current is just the right amount to make it burn at its efficient temperature.

Amps:
Area::
Volts:
Length

Thus, with a definite material such as tungsten, the cross section of the wire would determine the amount of current in amperes which can be handled efficiently, and the length of the wire would determine the amount of voltage which must be used to force the current through efficiently.

Life

Evaporation takes place gradually at any temperature increasing as the temperatures or the brightness of the filament become greater. A thousand hour lamp of a certain wattage, therefore, is less bright and has a longer filament than one which is rated to burn for ten hours.

Volts
&
Amperes

Roughly, also, the shorter the filament, the lower the voltage. An automobile headlamp may give off the same amount of light as an ordinary incandescent lamp, and the watts consumed may be equal, but the filament is proportionally shorter because it is made for six or twelve volts, as compared with 110, and likewise proportionally thicker because, for the same amount of wattage, it must carry approximately sixteen times the amount of current.

Voltage
Variation

Any reduction in the voltage of the current by outside means will diminish the brightness of the filament very rapidly at the start, and make it cease to glow, after passing from the white through yellow and red to out. But there still may be as much as twenty percent of the voltage working to cause a proportionate amount of current to flow in the filament.

B. FILAMENT DIMENSIONS AND OUTPUT (THOUSAND-HOUR LIFE, 115 VOLTS).

Lamp	Filament diameter	Length	Lumens per watt
10 watt	.0006"	16"	7.6
50 watt	.00162"	17.5"	8.9
100 watt	.00259"	21.6"	15.2
1000 watt	.0118"	40"	20.5
2000 watt	.015"	48"	23

---

* See lamp catalogs for the great range of types and details.
** See texts on electricity for further description.

C. FILAMENT MOUNTING AND BURNING POSITION

In order to avoid as much as possible the loss of light output in the form of heat by convection and conduction, all filaments are coiled and mounted so that the coils do not sag unduly during the course of the life of the lamp. The purpose for which the lamp is to be used, furthermore, determines the filament shape and mounting. The filament must have support because heat tends to make it sag, and naturally it is connected at both ends to the lead-in wires which also serve as supports. The supports must allow for contraction and expansion of the filament, must be embedded in a non-conducting material and insulated from each other. This is one of the chief problems facing the lamp manufacturers, and to a considerable degree it determines the range of burning angles for each type of lamp.

Inasmuch as the filament must be in a definite optical position with respect to reflectors and lenses, where different sizes and shapes of lamps are to be used in the same instrument from time to time, the filament height or light center length (L. C. L.) is important. This is measured in the case of the screw-base lamps from the center of the filament to the button in the end of the base. With prefocus-base lamps, it is measured from the center of the filament to the fins on the base.

1. <u>Corona</u>. The most common form of mounting is the ring or loop, which is called Corona (C-9, flat ring; C-7, in a ring formed by loops between supports). This is normally used in all inside-frosted standard lamps; any burning position. But in the larger sizes, particularly with the C-7 form, base-up burning is required because of the large loops. It is generally used in wide-angle flood lights and strips.

2. <u>Line</u>. The line filament C-8 is used primarily in T- (tubular) shaped bulbs. The output of the lamp, due to extending the filament, is invariably low, somewhere between 7 and 10 lumens per watt. A recent development using a coiled-coil (known as CC-6) has been made available in certain intermediate sizes. This form of mounting improves the efficiency of the lamp considerably. Burning position, any. It is generally used in strips.

3. <u>Barrel</u>. The first form of concentrated filament was built in what is called the barrel shape, known as C-5. This is generally enclosed in a G- (globular) shaped bulb, which, due to the closeness of the base to the filament, cannot be burned base up. It is used primarily in spotlights and concentrated-beam floodlights, and generally equipped with a screw base.

4. <u>Mono-and Biplane</u>. A more recent type in the concentrated form of filament mounting is the monoplane (C-13). This is available in G and T types of bulbs. The concentration has been further increased by mounting the filament in a biplane form, so that the coils of one plane are opposite the spaces between coils in the other (C-13D). These are used in spotlight and projection instruments and their burning position is invariably limited, due to the filament mounting and bulb size.

D. THE BULB

In order to prevent the filament from evaporating too rapidly, due to oxidation, it is surrounded by glass bulbs of different forms. In the type B the air is simply exhausted (10, 15, and 25-watt lamps). In the type C, the air is exhausted and the space filled with a combination of nitrogen and argon gas to permit the filament to burn at a high temperature without evaporation. In some of the larger sizes, for special purposes, a special glass called Corex is being used. This permits a smaller bulb than would be possible with ordinary glass because of the heat involved in operation.

1. <u>Wattage</u>. A good lamp catalog lists most of the available wattages in the various shaped bulbs, but there are a number of forms which are not listed because they have not yet passed the rigid tests which qualify them to carry the trade name. A supplementary list can always be obtained by writing to one of the lamp companies.

2. <u>Color</u>. Lamp catalogs indicate also the range of colors that can be had in the various lamp sizes. Generally, the natural-color glass bulb in 15, 25, and 40-watt, "A" shape, can be

had in the A and P.S. shapes in special colors up to 1500 watts.

3. Shape. The shape of the bulb is indicated by letters which generally are an abbreviation of a recognizable form; "T" for "tubular", "G" for "globular", and "P. S." for "pear-shaped". "A" refers to the inside frosted general service lamp. The diameter of the bulb is listed in 1/8's of an inch; for example: a G-40 is a globular-shaped bulb, 5 inches in diameter.

E   THE BASE See Appendix III

The mechanical means of mounting and connecting the lamp to the socket is called the base. In the screw form:

Miniature for low voltage—3/8" diameter.
Candelabra—1/2"—up to 15 w.
Intermediate—5/8"—low wattages.
Medium—1"—up to 300w. in P. S. shape, 400w. in G shape.
Mogul—1 1/2"—300 to 2000w.

In the prefocus form: Intermediate (Bayonet)—75-100w. G shape. Medium—100-750w. G and T shapes. Mogul—1000-2000w. G and T shapes.

In the bi-post form: Medium—500w. T. Mogul—1000, 1500, 2000, 3000, 5000, and 10,000w. (T shape base up or down, and G shape base down burning.)

The lumiline lamp has a special type of base with a contact at each end.

F.   LIFE

The rated life of the lamp is based on the average burning hours at the voltage stamped on the bulb until the filament reaches 80 percent of its efficiency in output or more realistically until the filament fails.

The average burning hours for the
A and P.S. lamps is 750 and 1000. G-type is 200 and 800. T-type is 50 to 200, and, in special cases, 500. Reflector type is 2000.

The effect of voltage on light output is, roughly: one percent over the rated amount stamped on the bulb, gives 3 1/2 percent more lumens in output, but decreases the life 13 percent, and vice versa.

G.   HEATING EFFECT

From 88 to 96 percent of the energy supplied to the lamp is dissipated in the form of heat. Instruments should be manufactured and mounted so that the fire hazard is reduced to a minimum, and constructed to provide ample ventilation for the lamp. Asbestos insulated wires are used within all instruments. Inflammable objects should not come in contact with the lamp or even the instrument housing it while in use.

III. THE REFLECTOR LAMP

In the reflector lamp, of which the sealed-beam headlight lamp is a well-known example, optical characteristics are given the light emanation from the filament by making a portion of the bulb itself a reflector shape and surface. The lamp is a complete optical instrument which, although discarded when the filament fails, is most economical under many conditions because of low initial cost. There appears to be a growing use of these lamps in the theatre because of their compactness and efficiency. There are three forms available in varying wattages but only the spot and flood have been used to any extent in the theatre. The Birdseye Company first developed this type of lamp and used silver on the inside of the bulb. Now G. E. and Westinghouse and others make three of the forms in a range of wattages and the reflector is of aluminum "sputtered" on the inside of the bulb. In all cases the bulb is given a slight degree of etching to break up the filament image.

In stage lighting these lamps should be mounted in a protective housing (with a universal joint where they are used as floods or spotlights) and equipped with a flat stripped or cast roundel of colored glass, or spread lens in a holder which can be clipped to the lamp or mounted in the protecting hood. Louvers are also available.

A. SPOTLIGHT AND FLOODLIGHT LAMPS (R for reflector). Blown glass, R-30 in the 75 watt size, R-40 in the 150, 300 watt, and 500 watt, R-56 750 and R-60 1000 watt, giving approximately 10 beam candle power per watt for the flood type (40° beam) and 50 beam candle power for the spotlight type (20° beam).

B. PROJECTOR LAMPS Hard glass type PAR-38 (PAR for parabolic) 75 and 150 watt size in both the spot and the flood, gives approximately 50 percent more beam candle power but a narrower beam, and can be used out-of-doors. PAR-46 200 watt, PAR-56 300 watt and 500 watt PAR-64 are also available in wide, medium and narrow beam.

C. SIDE SILVERED LAMP Generally in a T-10, 6 1/2" length, using a short line filament mounted off center in a half silvered tube. This gives a narrow beam parabolic effect on one axis and a wide spread on the other. The bulb is lightly frosted to give a smooth spread. It can be had in 25, and 40 watts. A spring tab on the base permits positioning in the screw socket.

IV. THE ARC LIGHT

Although the arc light, generally built into a spotlight hood is becoming less and less used, there are occasions, such as when an intense beam of very white light, particularly for slide or effect projection, follow-spot work, and when strong ultra-violet rays are needed, that the carbon arc light still has its place.

When two terminals of an electric circuit are pressed together in a loose contact, and then separated, the heat produced will create an arc. If the terminals are made of carbon or some other material which vaporizes below the melting point, the arc sets up a stream of ionized electrode (terminal) material which maintains a flow of electricity as through a conductor.

The electrons, passing from the negative electrode, bombard the tip of the positive and create an intense white light at the point. The amount of current depends somewhat upon the electrode material and resistance of the gap for the voltage in use. The arc flame gives relatively no light. It is the crater formed which really serves as a source. As the electrode material becomes vaporized, the terminals must be moved together to keep the gap constant.

Direct current is by all odds the best because it keeps a constant stream of electrons going in one direction, and the crater forms on what is called the positive carbon. This indicates that the positive carbon is larger than the negative, and for smoothness in operation it has a core of material different from its body. The negative carbon is small (and sometimes metal coated).

A fixed resistance or rheostat is used in a series with the arc to balance the flow of current as the gap varies, and to absorb the rush of current when the carbons are brought together for "striking". This is the way the arc is started. The arc cannot be dimmed except by flooding the spot and the irising it down at the same time.

A. CONSTRUCTION

Carbons are mounted end to end vertically (or on a slant) or at an angle to each other to let the crater face the lens or reflector. Carbons are of a size to carry the current which is permitted to pass between the rheostat and the gap: 1/2" diameter-50 amperes; 3/4"-100 amperes; 1 1/4"-150 amperes, for the positive carbon and 1/4", 3/8", and 1/2" respectively for the negative carbon.

The feed mechanism permits adjusting the carbons in relation to each other to keep them on axis with lens in the spotlight, and to keep them at the proper spacing. A disconnect switch is always mounted on the stand. The larger arcs are automatically fed, but each type requires an operator. Inasmuch as the arc must form on the positive carbon, the direction of the current is important. Connectors must be tested or keyed so as to guarantee this direction. Each carbon is connected by flexible asbestos-covered wires, and the connections are insulated from the feed mechanism by mica plates.

V. FLUORESCENT LAMP

The brilliant fluorescence of certain chemicals due to stimulation by ultra violet radiation is an efficient means of producing (relatively) cold light. In the last few years the lamp companies have developed a line of tubular lamps which are coated inside with powder which fluoresce in different colors under the impulse of a mercury (or neon, for red and gold only) arc.

In the hot cathode or preheat form they operate most efficiently around 70° and tend to go out because of the condensation of the mercury gas below 40°. They give off between 20 and 60 lumens per watt (averaging 40 for the daylight and 3500° white.)

They can be had in red, gold, pink, warm tone, soft-, warm-, and cool-white, daylight, blue and green but they are all distinctly short in the red end of the spectrum, probably as much as the normal incandescent light is in the blue. A combination of equal wattages in the fluorescent and incandescent tends to offset this deficiency, but emphasizes the yellow. Deluxe warm white and cool white give 15 to 30% less light but almost a normal amount of red.

They can be had in 6, 12, 14, 18, 24, 36, 48, and 60 inch lengths in the low voltage form and up to 96 feet in length in cold cathode high voltage type. The tubes are 1 inch in diameter for the 14, 18, and 36 inch; 1 1/2 inches for the 18, 24, and 48 inch; and 2 1/8 inches for the 60 inch. The smaller diameters average 10 watts per foot and the 2 1/8 inch size about 20 watts per foot. Cold cathode tubes are about 1/2" to 1" in diameter and average between 3 and 6 watts per foot. Continuous double tubing up to 48' (out and back) and bends to fit curved coves or shapes are practical.

Slimline tubes (single pin—instant start) are available in all colors and a range of operating currents. (120-200-300, —425 and 600 milliamps for the 96" tubes only). 42" and 64" T-6; 72" and 96" T-8; 48", 72" and 96" T-12; are the sizes generally available.

Efficient as these tubes are, they have very little use so far in the theatre because each requires a ballast (high voltage, a transformer for lengths up to 96') and unless used with a lagging phase control in the 2 lamp type, they produce some stroboscopic effect (flicker). The tubes work best on alternating current. Their chief drawback from the point of view of the theatre is the fact that only a special rapid start lamp with a constantly heated filament and the cold cathode type can be dimmed.* They are relatively expensive to replace, but they are guaranteed to last more than 7500 hours in the hot cathode type and more than 10,000 hours in the cold cathode type.

---

*Special ballasts and electronic or auto transformer controls for dimming rapid start 48" T-12 lamps can be had but they still show a slight jump on and off at the low end.

2. INSTRUMENTS

The instrument serves as a housing for the light source (generally an electric lamp) and a means for making its rays of emanation useful. The sun, due to its power of radiation, is able to send light out in all directions and still give ample illumination. Artificial sources are not ordinarily powerful enough to give adequate illumination by direct emanation, nor is it efficient to waste the rays of light that are given out in directions that are not useful for lighting definite objects. Likewise, the position of open light sources in relation to the field of vision is such that glare offsets the lighting of objects within that field. For these reasons sources are housed in instruments.

Through the application of optical laws and mechanical principles in cooperation with the characteristics of the practical sources, these instruments are designed to produce a variety of intensities, colors, and distributions. In this manner, artificial lighting may approach the natural effects under which vision has developed. Inasmuch as there is no elaborate instrument, emulating the sun, to give naturalistic lighting, any lighting layout involves the use of several instruments of different types, rather than the arbitrary though possibly more simple choice of efficient fixtures such as are generally employed in commercial and industrial lighting layouts.

Light is the raw material which is made useful by instruments. These can be effective only when designed in accordance with special optical laws which govern the control of light radiation.

The average student is sufficiently aware of the general optical laws as a matter of every-day information to make it unnecessary to include here more than a bare outline to crystallize and relate and to draw examples which will refresh the memory. Furthermore, it is unnecessary, except for the advanced student, to delve into the general Physics of the subject treated in detail in the average textbook.

Inasmuch as instruments use reflectors, lenses, and absorbing cutoffs such as mats, louvers, shutters, and color mediums, it seems wise to anticipate the discussion of the various types with the laws which govern the use of each one of these accessories.

I. VISUAL RADIATION

A. THE NATURE AND TRANSMISSION OF LIGHT

1. Intensity. Candle Power. Intensity is the amount of radiant energy. Of all types of radiant energy only that which falls within a small zone of wave lengths is capable of stimulating the eye. The amount of light is expressed in terms of candle power, symbol "I".

2. Color.
   a. Spectrum. White light contains all the colors of the spectrum in a certain balance of intensities. Any color effect is due to the predominance of the wave lengths which stimulate a certain color sense in the eye. A rainbow is merely a result of separating the wave lengths contained in the sun's rays so that they can be seen adjacent to one another. If a section of the rainbow or spectrum were treated so that each color were superimposed on the same area, white light, like the original beam from the sun would appear.

   b. Primary Colors. The eye sees color as a composite result of all the wave lengths which are present. The primary colors of light are those three which, when added together in equal quantities on a surface, will produce white light. These are different from those used in pigment mixing, because pigment appears a certain color by reason of its ability to absorb certain rays and to reflect others. It has been found that red, green, and purplish blue, when mixed together in various amounts, are able to produce almost any tint or shade of light.

   c. Color Definitions. The definition of color in light can be expressed in terms of the quantities of each of the three primaries present, or the dominant hue; its degree of freedom of admixture with white light, saturation; and the third component which corresponds to intensity, but is expressed as brightness, or as a color cut off.

14

3. Distribution.

   a. <u>Straight-Line Radiation.</u> Light rays are created by a source and go out in space in all directions in straight lines. When this is a theoretical point source, the amount of light in each direction is the same. If, however, as is always the case, the source has definite dimensions, such as the line filament in a tubular lamp, obviously more light is going to be projected out in some directions than in others, generally perpendicular to the largest dimensions of the source.

   b. <u>Shadow.</u> The straight-line characteristics of the rays are so obvious and well known that it is hardly necessary to call attention to the fact that the edge of a shadow can always be determined by drawing a straight line between the source, the point where the rays are intercepted and the surface upon which the shadow falls.

   c. <u>Lumen, Foot-Candle.</u> Rays going out in all directions, like radii of a great sphere, become less dense as they proceed from the source, in the order of the square of the distance. The same rays falling on a square foot area at a certain distance would cover 4 square feet at twice the distance. Therefore, the intensity per unit area would be one-quarter as great. The number or density of the light rays in a beam intercepted by a unit area, at unit distance (from a one-candle power source) is called a lumen; thus, the amount of illumination on a surface one foot from a one candle source is a lumen per square foot or a foot-candle, symbol "i".

   d. <u>Inverse-Square Law.</u> With any light source at any distance the intensity of illumination in foot-candles or lumens per square foot is the result of the candle power of the lamp divided by the distance squared, $i=I/d^2$. The effect of this can easily be seen in the natural grading of the illumination at various distances from a nearby source, but here the factor of angle of illumination further causes grading in proportion to the cosine which equals 1 with perpendicular incidence and 0 at 90^0. Thus $i=I/d^2$ x the cosine of the angle.

   e. <u>Distribution Curve.</u> The variable density of rays emanating from a source or instrument can be indicated graphically in the form of a distribution curve. This is simply a curve at a chosen scale which represents the relative candle power amount in each direction from a source. It is actually a three-dimensional form, but as most instruments give a symmetrical beam, a cross section through the source on the axis of the beam shows the typical distribution. The curve can be laid out on a polar graph (radiating lines generally at 5-degree intervals with concentric circles around the radiating points at equal distances; the concentric circles are each assigned candle power values), or on a coordinate graph (the vertical scale for candle power values and the horizontal for degrees from the axis).

   f. <u>Illumination Curve.</u> This can be laid out on a coordinate graph (the vertical scale for the number of foot-candles on a line in the illuminated plane and the horizontal scale for the linear measure along this line).

   g. <u>Reflection, Refraction, & Absorption.</u> Inasmuch as light rays normally travel out in all directions, some of the rays must be reflected or refracted so that they are turned into a useful direction by means of equipment surrounding the lamp in the fixture. In the process of reflection and refraction, a certain number of rays are absorbed, depending upon the coefficients of reflection or transmission, which are characteristic of the materials used.

B. REFLECTION

1. <u>Types of Reflection.</u> Reflection occurs in four different forms: (1) regular reflection similar to that given by a mirror; (2) spread reflection similar to that given by a silver screen or a matt metallic surface; (3) diffuse reflection similar to that given by a vast majority of surfaces, the most typical being white blotting paper; and (4) specular or mixed reflection, such as that given by hard shiny surfaces which show high lights, but otherwise give diffuse reflection.

a. <u>Regular Reflection</u>. Regular reflection takes place when a ray of light strikes some mirror-like surface and is turned back at an angle equal and in the same plane as the incident direction. By shaping the mirror, the reflected rays can be made to take definite direction. The coefficients of reflection of materials used for this type of equipment are listed in the following table:

Silver	85 to 92%	Aluminum	60 to 70%
Alzak	80 to 87%	Chromium	55 to 65%

b. <u>Spread Reflection</u>. Inasmuch as no filament is a point source, irregular filament images are likely to result from mirrored surfaces so that surfaces which give spread reflection are often used. Etched aluminum dissipates somewhat the directionality given by the shape of the reflector, but it does tend to soften the effect and to remove the irregular images. A spread reflector has numerous microscopic surfaces which lie only on the average plane of the reflector as a whole. Therefore, the direction in each case is slightly out of line, but the majority of rays follow the direction given by the reflector. The material most often used to produce spread reflection is etched aluminum or mat Alzak, which have a coefficient of reflection between 75 and 85%.

c. <u>Diffuse Reflection</u>. Diffuse-reflection occurs where the reflecting surface redirects the illumination more or less in all directions. It consists of an infinite number of small planes at an angle to each other, although the general surface may be flat or follow a definite curve. This obviously eliminates any directionality and tends to offset the effect of the shape of any reflector. White blotting paper may have a coefficient of reflection of between 75% and 90%.

d. <u>Specular or Mixed Reflection</u>. A blue vase appears blue by diffuse reflection, but the high lights are the color of the illuminating sources. This indicates that many hard shiny surfaces give a combination of regular and diffuse reflection. It is sometimes called mixed reflection, and the word "specular" is loosely applied to all shiny surfaces.

2. <u>Selective Reflection</u>. The most characteristic feature of diffusing surfaces is their ability to provide selective reflection. In other words, a colored surface absorbs certain rays in the incident light and will reflect only those which are similar to its pigment color. The name given to a pigment color is a result of our seeing its effect ordinarily under white light. A red surface absorbs all rays in the incident light except the red rays which it reflects. As a result, the coefficient of reflection of any colored surface is likely to be low, and as gray or black is introduced, not only selective reflection but absorption takes place. A gray fabric will obviously reflect only part of the light which falls on it. A black velvet fabric will absorb almost 100% of the light.

3. <u>Coefficients of Reflection</u>. It is necessary to differentiate somewhat between selective and ordinary reflection, and the following table gives the list of coefficients of reflection for a typical color under white light.

White	75 to 90%	Dark Green	17 to 20%
Light Blue	35 to 50%	Dark Red	10 to 15%
Gray	15 to 60%	Dark Blue	3 to 10%
		Black Paint	1 to 5%

4. <u>Colored Light on Pigment</u>. When the light source does not create white light, only the coefficients for white, gray, and black hold. Under any conditions where color is used in the light, it must be realized that any pigment surface it falls upon will not have a normal appearance. A red light thrown on a red surface will make it seem much more brilliant only because other colored surfaces surrounding it will not be able to reflect the same amount of light that they would under white light giving equal illumination. If a green light is directed on a red surface, there is nothing in the red pigment except its impurities which permit reflection. Specular reflection may be present, as is almost always the case, particularly where any oil paint is used. Small particles on the surface may act as regular mirrors and reflect some of the green light. Therefore, the amount of reflection, under

green light, may be as low as from 1% to 5%.

C. REFRACTION

A ray of light passing obliquely from one transparent medium to another is usually bent at the surface separating the two. This is called refraction. On passing into a denser medium the ray is bent toward a line drawn perpendicularly to the entering plane, and away from it as it passes through the emerging plane into a lighter medium.

1. Index of Refraction. The amount of bending depends upon the relative speed of light in the two mediums concerned. The slowness of light in any medium, relative to that of air is called the index of refraction of that medium, and is indicated by the symbol "n". This is the reciprocal of the velocity, so that when air is taken as the standard of 1, Water is 1.33, crown glass is 1.53, and flint glass 1.63. These figures are the index for the central, or yellow wave length zone, of the spectrum.

2. Angles. The ratio of the sine of the angle of incidence to the sine of refraction is constant for any wave length, no matter what the inclination of the incident ray. The incident, refracted, and reflected rays are all in the same plane.

3. Perpendicular Incidence shows no bending or refraction.

4. Parallel Faces. A ray entering a dense medium with parallel faces is offset, but emerges in a direction parallel to the original direction.

5. Total Reflection. Total reflection takes place in a dense medium when a ray meets the surface of a lighter medium at such an angle that the refracted ray is 90 degrees to the normal. At this and greater incident angles the ray cannot emerge so it is reflected back. The critical angle in crown glass is about 42 degrees. The outer surface of the denser medium makes an almost perfect reflecting surface. This is the principle used in the reflecting prisms in binoculars and many other types of optical apparatus.

D. ABSORPTION

Whenever a ray of light strikes an object or a dense medium, some of the incident light is absorbed in the process of reflection or transmission. Non-selective absorption takes place when the body or medium is of a neutral tone, and in this case the reflected or transmitted light is of the same color content as the incident rays.

Selective absorption takes place when the body or medium on which the radiation falls is colored. In this case wave lengths of similar color to the object are reflected or transmitted. The rest are absorbed.

The amount of reflection or transmission is the reciprocal of the absorption. For convenience sake this is called selective reflection and transmission, and the amounts are stated in terms of percentage of incident light—coefficient of reflection or transmission.

Selective Transmission. Similar to selective reflection, selective transmission takes place when a white or colored light passes through a transparent or translucent medium of a definite color composition. See Coefficients of Transmission.

II. ACCESSORIES

The practical application of optical laws makes itself evident in the form of various parts of the instruments which make the rays of emanation from the light source useful. Unfortunately there is little standardization, so that only typical examples are listed in the following paragraphs.

A. REFLECTORS

Shape. Reflectors take the form of circular, elliptical, and parabolic sections for the most part. Some are designed as a combination of these forms. In manufacture, they are generally spun so that they take the symmetrical form and are called spherical, ellipsoidal, and parabolic shapes.

Size, Material, Surface. Each one of these forms has an optical center at a point on the axis where the filament of the lamp should lie. The sizes are dictated by the size of the bulb and the amount of light to be gathered. The position of the reflector is likewise dictated by the direction the rays are to assume and the means for mounting the lamp. The material is generally metal (since glass offers a breakage hazard) and it must be of such a nature as to stand the intense heat of the lamp over a long period of time. Reflectors are generally plated or given a finish which has a high coefficient or reflection. In the order of importance they are: specular alzak, for shiny reflectors, and etched alzak or aluminum for spread reflectors. Diffuse reflection can be given by mat white paint, where the shape of the reflector is unimportant. Therefore materials used for this type of reflection are not listed here further.

The reflector is the most efficient accessory for gathering rays of light. Regular reflection tends to give filament images, so that some reflectors are given a slightly irregular shape or mat treatment. To the extent that the treatment approaches a diffuse reflector control is correspondingly limited. The rays of direct emanation not gathered by the reflector must usually be absorbed by louvers or other accessories. Reflectors with a broadspread distribution give a high lumen output; those which concentrate the rays give lower efficiency but a higher degree of control.

1. Spherical.

    a. Light source at center of curvature

    b. When the light source lies on the axis at one-half the radius, approximately a 60 degree angle serves as a parabolic form.

    c. Used primarily in spotlights, of a radius so that it can be mounted from 1/4 to 1 inch behind the bulb, and of a diameter (of the face) large enough to redirect the rays of light through the light center to the extreme edges of the lens when the lamp is at flood focus.

2. Ellipsoidal.

    a. A half full ellipsoid or one which subtends a solid angle of 270° about the light source. When the filament is at the focal center, the rays are redirected to a conjugate focal point which lies on the axis at the same distance beyond the plane of the minor axis as the focal point lies behind it.

    b. The distance from the focal point to the front edge of the half reflector is equal to half the major axis.

    When a = half the major axis
    When b = half the minor axis $\Bigg\}$ then $\dfrac{x^2}{a^2} + \dfrac{y^2}{b^2} = 1$
    When x = dist. from minor axis
    When y = dist. from major axis

    c. In floods due to the direction of the last reflected ray at the front edge of the reflector on one side being parallel to the last ray of direct emanation as it passes the opposite side, a color medium can be moved across the face of the instrument without showing a distinct line. A card can be used as a crude mechanical dimmer by moving it across the face of the instrument from one side to the other.

    d. Used in the ellipsoidal reflector spotlight, with a small T-type high powered lamp, 6, 8, 14 and 16 inch diameter sizes. Used in flood lights in an etched aluminum finish with P.S. lamps between 10 and 18 inches in diameter.

18

3.   Parabolic   (Should be called "paraboloid")

   a.   With the light-point source at the focal center, all the rays of direct emanation picked
       up by the reflector will be reflected parallel to the axis.   This is the type of reflector
       used in automobile headlights and searchlights.

> When f=the focal length, x is the distance from
> the reflector to a point on the axis, and y is the
> perpendicular distance from this point on the
> axis to the reflector, then $4fx=y^2$

   b.   When the source is moved forward from the principal focus, the reflected rays con-
       verge;   diverge, when behind, and there will be a dark spot in the center of the beam.

   c.   Due to the size of the filament, there is always a certain spread to the beam, because
       certain parts of the filament are ahead of the principal focus, and other parts are be-
       hind.   The rays from the extreme edges of the filament to a certain point on the re-
       flector form what is called the acceptance angle.   Due to the fact that all parts of the
       reflector contribute to all parts of the area lighted, a color medium can be moved
       across the face of the instrument without showing a distinct line, and as with the ellip-
       soidal unit also, a card can be made to serve as a crude mechanical dimmer by going
       through the same process.

   d.   This reflector is the chief accessory in a projector.   Due to its critical characteris-
       tics, it tends to show filament images.   However, these are not always distracting.
       They are sometimes corrected by forming flats on the reflectors or giving it a slight-
       ly diffusing surface.   Due to its short focal length, generally less than 120 degrees of
       direct emanation can be gathered.   The rest must be absorbed in the hood, eliminated
       by louvers, redirected by a spherical reflector, or picked up by a short-focal-length
       lens.

4.   Compound Parabolic-Spherical-Parabolic.

   a.   This reflector tends to gather more rays of light and still stay within reasonable size.
       The front parabolic section has a short-focal length which would fall within the bulb,
       but it stops at a plane through the center of the lamp perpendicular to its axis.   At this
       point, the spherical section starts and extends backward to a point where the rays will
       be redirected through the filament to the front of the first parabolic section.   Here the
       second long-local-length parabolic section joins and completes the form of the reflector.

   b.   This form, although it gathers up to 240 degrees of emanation, tends to show filament
       images more, because of the larger acceptance angles, and loses some light by multi-
       ple reflection from the spherical reflector.

5.   Cylindrical Reflector with Circular, Elliptical, or Parabolic Sections.   The characteristics
    of this reflector on the plane perpendicular to the axis (cross section), are the same as
    those listed above, but the rays emanating either side of this plane, spread more and more
    until they approach the reflection given by a plane reflector.

6.   Paracyl.   A running reflector with a half circular section continuing into a half parabolic
    section.   A compact means of giving a projected fan of light from a line, or a standard
    source.

7.   Irregular Shapes.   These are generally compound reflectors designed to use the irregular
    distribution given by most filament forms to produce a definite beam pattern which is not
    symmetrical.   Their design is based on the principles laid out in the previous paragraphs,
    and is generally found in special instruments.

B. LENSES

Lenses are generally round segments of a sphere with a flat face, made of crown glass (plano-convex, converging type). This is the basic accessory of the spotlight. The radius of curvature is about .52 times the focal length.

1. **Principal Focus.** The principal focus lies on the major axis at such a distance from the lens that the rays emanating from this point, upon passing through the lens, would converge to a direction parallel to the major axis. The distance to this point from the principal plane (generally 2/3 of the distance through the lens from the flat face or at the center of the round face when measured from the opposite side) is the focal length.

2. **Focal Points.** The relation between the positions of the light source or the object (generally a lantern slide) and the point where the transmitted rays form an image, is determined by the lens formula:

> When p = the distance from the object to the
> principal plane of the lens, q = the distance
> from the principal plane to the image, and f =
> the focal length of the lens; then $1/p + 1/q = 1/f$.

The object and the image lie at conjugate focal points on opposite sides of the lens. When the light source lies inside the focal length, the rays on passing through the lens will form a beam of a definite angle that seems to come from an enlarged source (the image) on the incident side of the lens. In using the formula, the q distance in this case is negative. Also when p = 2f it is = to q.

3. **Construction of images.** It is possible to lay out graphically the position of images in relation to the position of the light source by considering two significant rays of emanation coming from the source. The one passing through the principal focus will be bent parallel to the major axis on emerging. The ray passing through the center of the lens will not be altered in direction because the two faces are approximately parallel at the center. These two rays meet at the point where the image is formed.

4. **Types.**

   a. **Converging.** Double-convex, plano-convex (described above), and meniscus (crescent-shaped). All lenses of the same diameter and same focal length in these types are the same thickness in the center. The Fresnel lens is a form of the plano-convex type. It is generally of extremely short-focal-length and stepped so that a section of the lens is saw-toothed in appearance. All that has been done here is to remove parallel faced sections of the glass which do not change the direction of the ray, and to step the various sections of the curved surface so that they maintain the same angle with the plane face, zone for zone, as they would have in a very thick lens. These lenses are generally made of heat-resisting glass, and their focal length is about half their diameter.

   b. **Diverging.** These are of the concave type seldom used in stage-lighting equipment.

   c. **Cylindrical.** These have a cross section similar to the plano-convex type and a longitudinal section with parallel faces.

   d. **Spread.** Spread lenses or roundels consist of fluted glass which refracts the light on one axis. These are ordinarily used to spread the concentrated beam of a parabolic reflector a definite number of degrees from a circular pattern into an oval or wide band, as the cover glass of a headlight.

5. **Use.**

   a. Ordinary spotlights, Fresnel spots, and ellipsoidal reflector units have lenses as one of their primary accessories.

Plano-convex spots:

> 250 to 400-w. 5" (diameter), by 8", 9", and 10" focal lengths,
> 500 and 1000-w. 6" by 8", 9", 10", and 12",
> 1500-w. 8" by 10", 12", 14".

Fresnel:

> 75, 100 and 200-w. 3" by approximately 2 1/4" focal length,
> 250, 500, and 750-w. 6" by approximately 3 1/2",
> 1000 and 1500-w. 8" by approximately 4 3/4",
> 2000-w. 10", 12",
> 5000-w. 14", 16",
> 10000-w. 20".

Ellipsoidal reflector spots use 4 1/2", 6", and 8" for the 250-1000-w., 8" for the 1000 and 2000-w., 10" for 750-1000-w. and 12" for the 3000-w., 16" for 2100-w., 60 v. A pair of medium-focal-length plano-convex lenses, or one short-focal-length inside stepped (convex fresnel) lens, is used for wide or medium beam spread. One medium-focal-length lens is used for medium or narrow beam spreads.

b. <u>Projection or Effect Machine.</u> This machine is described more completely under special instruments in Section III of this chapter. In its simplest form the spotlight is used as a source; a thick condensing lens as a dutchman; and a pair of lenses as an objective for creating the image of the slide.

c. <u>Other Uses.</u> Occasionally a Fresnel lens is used in front of the light source in a projector as an intensifier to gather the rays which are not picked up by the reflector, but these rays are normally absorbed by louvers or returned to the filament by a spherical reflector.

C. DIFFUSERS

1. <u>Frosted Gelatin.</u> Any means of breaking up the beam of light to any degree by transmission serves as a diffuser. The means is generally a frosted gelatin which has a crystalline structure on one side. When the ray of light strikes the crystals, it is reflected and refracted in all directions, and thus each portion of the diffuser tends to become a new light source. The density of the frosting determines the degree of diffusion.

2. <u>Soft Edging.</u> When used with plano-convex spotlights, a small quantity of oil or grease, rubbed into the surface in the center of the frost, will allow more direct transmission and yet soften the edge of the spotlight. Sometimes electricians prefer to cut out a small hole in the center of the frosted gelatin or simply to scratch the edges of the usual color medium, leaving the center clear.

3. <u>Roundels.</u> Clear and colored glass roundels (sometimes called color-lenses) are manufactured by many companies. They are used over the face of strip, or flood-lighting units as color filters and unless they are lined or mottled they do not change the direction of the rays, because the surfaces are parallel to each other.

D. CUTOFFS

In order to eliminate the rays which are not useful and which might cause a spill, absorbing mediums in the form of cutoffs are used as accessories to most instruments. These should be painted flat black as a rule, but even flat-black paint will reflect some light. A scored surface, one equipped with baffles, or lined with black velvet, will give greater absorption.

1. <u>Flippers, Shutters, Mats.</u> These are sheets of metal or opaque material used to shape the

21

beam of a spotlight. They are mounted in the color-frame slide and built so as to retain their position once they are set.

The plano-convex spotlight can be matted reasonably successfully to any shape. This is not true of the Fresnel type, but it is an essential part of the ellipsoidal reflector spotlight which uses the front lens or lenses as an objective and shutters or an iris or both at the gate position, as the object. By this means, a sharp image of the shape of the shutters or iris can frame the area lighted.

2. **The Iris.** This is a reducing mat used over the face of the arc spots and occasionally inside the ellipsoidal reflector spot. Its primary use is for follow-spot work where the diameter of the beam must be changed readily to cover different widths of area. It can be used with the arc spot as a dimmer where a narrow beam is being used. If the spotlight is flooded (moving the burner towards the lens) the intensity at the center of the beam will drop to 1/10 of its original amount, and if, at the same time, the iris is closed to keep the spread of the beam or the diameter of the area lighted the same, dimming can be effected mechanically.

3. **Funnel.** This is a cylindrical or rectangular shape serving as an extension to the hood of a spotlight to cut down side spill, particularly when a diffuser is being used over the face of the instrument. The inside of the funnel should be painted flat black, lined with black velvet or parallel baffles, to cut down internal reflection. Never use shiny black paint. The depth of the funnel depends upon the degree of control desired in relation to the space provided. Generally they are from 6 to 8 inches long.

4. **Louvers.** These consist of metal strips mounted in concentric rings parallel to the general direction of the useful rays of light, and are used primarily over the face of the projector to eliminate the direct emanation and to pass the parallel reflected rays. They do not direct the rays in any sense. A special form of sleeve, or cylindrical louver, can be used in the place of several shallow concentric rings over the face of a projector. Sometimes parallel louvers are mounted on swivels so that they can be used as flippers which give mechanical dimming. They close the entire face of the instrument when tipped perpendicularly to the direction of the rays. For greatest control, louvers should be painted flat black. They should be deep enough and mounted in relation to each other so that no direct emanation can come out of the face of the hood in unwanted directions. Inasmuch as no instrument produces strictly parallel rays, a louver always tends to reduce the output of efficiency in any instrument, sometimes as much as 50 percent.

E. COLOR MEDIUMS

When we wish to create colored light with a white-light source, it is necessary to filter out certain rays by the use of a color medium. The color transmission characteristics of such materials as glass, cellophane, gelatin, and a number of new plastic materials that are coming on the market, are the result of selective transmission. In other words, a blue glass will select only the blue rays from the incident white light for transmission, and its coefficient of transmission indicates the percentage allowed to pass. Above the wattage obtainable in natural-colored lamps (40, 60-100 watts on special order), it is necessary to use color mediums over the face of the instrument. Generally they are mounted in color frames which, in the large sizes, have cross wires to support the expanse of flexible medium. Because of the lack of standardization in color terminology, the exactness of color tone can only be established eventually by a spectro-photometric analysis of each color medium in terms of a curve which illustrates the proportion of each wave length of the spectrum present in the transmitted light of any color medium. This is called a color cutoff.

1. **Specifications.**

   a. **High Transmission.** Color mediums should be pure and highly transparent; they should have no gray in the pigment, and should be as thin as possible, so that as much energy in the particular zone of the spectrum concerned as possible is transmitted.

b. <u>Fastness.</u> All mediums except those made of glass tend to fade under the heat involved in operating the instrument. Blues and violets are particularly fugitive. The great advantage glass has over the other color mediums is that it does not fade.

c. <u>Strength.</u> Consistent with the amount of handling necessary. Film color mediums, such as gelatin, tend to shrink and become brittle after some time in use. Cellophane is stronger, but it is made in such thin sheets that it must be supported in a color frame. It is well to cut flat glass sheets into strips and mount them in a color frame, so that expansion and contraction due to heat is less liable to break them. Roundels are often made of heat-resisting glass. New plastic materials coming on the market, such as lumarith, can be had in various weights and tend to hold their color more satisfactorily than gelatin or cellophane.

d. <u>Noninflammability.</u> The Code specifies that color mediums should have an inflammability not greater than newsprint. This immediately eliminates celluloid and puts cellophane on the border line. Glass is obviously the best from this point of view.

e. <u>Nonhydroscopic.</u> Impervious to moisture.

f. <u>Variety.</u> Color mediums should be available in a variety of pure colors and tints. Glass roundels as a rule can be had only in red, green, blue, and amber. Recently, sheet glass in various tints has become available. Gelatin is still to be had in the greatest variety of shades and tints. Stronger types of filters, called Cinemord or Cinebex—more expensive varieties—are generally waterproof, stronger mechanically, and more "fast" than gelatin.

g. <u>Cost.</u> A primary determining factor in the use of color is the cost. Fastness and mechanical strength should be related to labor and material cost for replacement. Cellophane, gelatin, plastic materials, and glass are listed in the order of cost. Over a period of time, particularly where instruments are equipped with the same color medium constantly (footlights, border lights, background lights), it is interesting to see how much more economical the more expensive type of color medium is, even where a variety of productions is being put on; and it is for this reason that the Germans have consistently used glass as a color medium.

2. Terminology. One draw back in all color medium is the lack of standardization in names applied to the same color produced by different companies, and the lack of similarity between one batch and another. General Electric undertook to standardize this terminology in relation to gelatin. This code has been adopted by a number of companies. It is always best to order color mediums by number instead of by name, because of the lack of standardization, and also because one individual's interpretation may differ from another's. The numbers used here are Brigham.

3. Use. Following the standardization of terminology and basing the use on the three-color system, namely, that red, green, and blue as primary colors, when used in varying proportions will create, roughly, any shade or tint, such instruments as footlights, border lights, cyclorama foots, horizon lights, and occasionally the high-powered overheads, can be assigned definite colors. Primary colors transmit very little light, therefore it is advisable to use lighter tints wherever possible, and, if there is no problem of delicate balancing, it is better to pick a tint to be used with one circuit of lights, than to try to create it synthetically with two or more circuits equipped with deeper colors. However, the following numbers apply most generally.

a. <u>Footlights.</u>

For color mixing:	For higher transmission, less color:
No. 36, non-fade blue	No. 3, pink
No. 49, dark green	No. 56, light amber
No. 67, fire red	No. 26, light blue

b. **First Border Lights,** using lighter color, therefore obtaining greater transmission.

For color mixing:
No. 32, medium blue special
No. 48, medium green
No. 67,

For higher transmission—secondaries
No. 11, magenta
No. 58, medium amber
No. 41, moonlight blue (cyan blue)

c. **Cyc Overheads.**

For color mixing:
No. 36 or 37 dark blue
No. 49
No. 67

For direct color; less flexibility:
No. 26, light sky blue
No. 29, special blue
No. 36
No. 57, light amber

d. **Cyc Foots or Horizon Lights.**

For color mixing:
No. 32
No. 48
No. 67

For direct color:
No. 16, violet
No. 25, daylight blue
No. 26
No. 29
No. 41
No. 57

e. **Acting Area Lights.**

No. 1, frost
No. 2, light flesh pink
No. 3
No. 6, rose pink
        (generally too deep)
No. 17, special lavender
        Called Surprise Pink

No. 26
No. 29, for moonlight
No. 54, light straw
No. 57
No. 62, light scarlet

f. **Motivating Lights.**

For sunlight:
    Clear, 54, 62

For sunsets:
    No. 57
    No. 58
    No. 60, dark amber

For moonlight:
    No. 29, or
    No. 17 and No. 25
    No. 41 (never)

For fire:
    No. 60, dark amber
    No. 61, orange

For dimming with color:
    No. 75, neutral gray

g. **Special Effects.**

No. 9, duBarry pink
No. 14, rose purple
No. 18, medium lavender

No. 41, (Cyan blue), or any of the other colors
        previously mentioned.

4. Coefficients of Transmission of Gelatin (Approximate)

No.	1, frost	85%	No. 32, medium blue	5.5%
No.	2, light flesh pink	75	No. 36, dark blue	3
No.	3, flesh pink	65	No. 39, urban blue	1.5
No.	6, rose pink	32	No. 41, moonlight blue	6
No.	9, light magenta	53	No. 44, medium blue green	40.5
No.	11, medium magenta	26	No. 48, medium green	18
No.	14, purple	12	No. 49, dark green	4.5
No.	16, violet	11	No. 54, light straw	85
No.	17, special lavender	27.5	No. 27, amber	72
No.	18, medium lavender	17	No. 58, medium amber	64
No.	25, daylight blue	40	No. 60, dark amber	48
No.	26, light steel blue	35	No. 61, orange	39
No.	27, light blue	15	No. 62, light scarlet	70
No.	29, dark steel blue	20	No. 67, fire red	14
			No. 75, gray	24.5

5. Color Frames. In previous sections, attention has been given to the qualifications of the various types of color mediums that can be had. The film type of color medium needs support and must be mounted in a frame, and these are generally built of folded sheet metal with a slot for inserting the gelatin; with clips which hold it in position; or built in two parts so the gelatin can be clipped in with the cover in one position, or a color roundel held when the cover is turned over. The latter is equipped with a key when made for spread lenses to fit in the slot at the top of the lens. The frame should be larger than the opening of the face of the instrument so as not to cut off any light, and it must have sufficient width to hold the edges of the gelatin, even when it shrinks. In the larger sizes, some of which are made of wood, cross wires are used to support the gelatin.

Unfortunately there is very little standardization in the size of color frames so that a vast number of them have to be kept on hand to supply the colors for the various instruments that are to be used in each scene. It is not practical to try to change color mediums in a frame between scenes. The most ideal situation would be to have a complete choice of color mediums adjacent to each instrument other than those which are equipped with the three primary colors.

6. Color Boomerangs. Generally the arc follow spots, used in the booth in picture houses, are equipped with a magazine holding four or five color mediums. These can be pulled up mechanically over the face of the instrument at will. A suitable selection for acting area work would be No. 3, No. 17, No. 26, No. 54 or 58, and No. 62. For more spectacular effects, deeper colors should be used. It is also possible to rely on selective transmission by using two mediums at one time to get another color—thus, if No. 11, medium magenta, and No. 41, Cyan blue, are superimposed, a satisfactory blue is produced. If No. 41 and No. 58 are superimposed, a suitable green is created, and if No. 58 and No. 11 are superimposed, a satisfactory red is given. In addition to these, either No. 3, 17, 26, or 62 will give an adequate range where the number of frames is limited. Where spotlights are used in positions difficult of access, or where it is desirable to control the selection of color remotely from the switchboard, a magnetic or motor-driven control can be installed. This is limited to the choice of four or five definite colors, and it is a moderately expensive installation.

F. MOUNTING EQUIPMENT

In order to obtain the proper distribution and direction of light rays on the stage, instruments of all types must be mounted securely in a great variety of positions. Too often the structural layout of the building and the form of the setting limit the flexibility of position, or create a tendency to accept traditional practice, so that the proper distribution can be obtained only approximately.

Direction. The sum total of the direction of the light rays from all positions determines the form of the light distribution, and, ultimately, the register of high lights and shadows on the retina of the observer, no matter in what part of the audience he may be. The position more or less determines the type of instrument that will give the desired distribution, and also determines the amount of directability likely to be required of an instrument in any place. But inasmuch as most units serve in a number of positions, the directability requirements become more important.

Position. In order to place the different types of instruments in the proper positions in relation to the structural arrangements of the building, the form and openings in the setting, the hollow-ceiling beams, light pits, stands, towers, battens, and bridges are a part of the equipment of any adequate lighting layout. For the sake of convenience pipe battens are usually 1 1/2 inches in diameter. Stands are usually equipped with swing joints, and pierced with a hole to use a 1/2-inch bolt. Instruments are equipped with side studs (1/2-inch threaded shanks) or yokes with a swing joint pierced to take a 1/2-inch bolt.

Safety and Reliability. Instruments are usually heavy metal hoods equipped with certain fragile or delicate parts. They should be mounted so that no reasonable amount of jarring or vibration will in any way seriously affect their position. None of the parts should be liable to work loose and fall of their own weight. Thus, parts have to be strong and somewhat bulky. Joints should be clamped tightly—in the case of a pipe clamp, very tightly—but with a sticky action where rotation is not affected by gravity. The direction of the throw of light should not be altered when changing color mediums, or moving the lamp in the hood. The mounting may be such that the direction can be changed at will by relying on the sticky joints to hold the instruments in the new direction. Set bolts will lock a screw joint in position.

1. Mounting Means. It is unnecessary to take space here to describe thoroughly the various pieces of apparatus used for mounting instruments. The student should consult catalogs and carry out the typical practice listed under "3" of this section to familiarize himself with the use and variety of the parts listed below.

    a. Arm. A short piece of strap iron pierced at both ends to take a 1/2-bolt or a pipe equipped with a swing joint and a clamp. It is wise to standardize on 8, 12, and 18-inch lengths.

    b. Base. A cast-iron disc, tapped and threaded, which serves as a footing for an instrument when it rests on a flat surface, such as the stage floor, platform, or the bridge floor. The edge is generally pierced so that it can be screwed to the flat surface. It comes in sizes 6, 8, 10, 12, 16, and 18 inches in diameter.

    c. Boomerang. A tormentor pipe or a remotely operated multiple color frame changing mechanism.

    d. Bridge. Generally the bridge, hung over the stage just back of the procenium openings, is equipped with two fixed battens on its under side. The upright stanchions have swivels for side-stud mounting instruments, and sockets for raising instruments mounted on shafts.

    e. Clamps. Pipe clamps are used to hang instruments from pipe battens, and should be adjustable to take any size from a 1/2-inch to a 1 1/2-inch pipe. They use a set bolt or wing bolts, and come in the following forms: jaw with swing joint, jaw with pipe threads (3/4-inch), or shaft with set screw, and the two-piece clamp, the cover of which is arched and can be turned over to clamp small pipes. This type uses two bolts or two wing bolts.

    f. Hand-Set Wheel. This serves as a manually operated tightener for side-stud mounting in place of an ordinary nut.

    g. Knee or Elbow. This is heavy strap iron bent in the shape of a right angle and pierced at each end to take a 1/2-inch bolt, or a pipe elbow equipped at each end with a swing joint or clamp.

h. <u>Leather Washer.</u> A 2 to 3-inch leather disk giving a sticky joint.

i. <u>Pipe.</u> Pipe is always measured by its inside diameter. This is determined by the strength required and is generally provided in 1, 1 1/4, and 1 1/2-inch sizes, for battens, 1/2, 3/4, and 1-inch pipe is used for shafts and sockets in stands. A liberal supply of short lengths of pipe simplifies many mounting problems. The ends should be threaded, and couplers, "T", swing joints, and clamps can be then fitted to these various lengths. A Stilson wrench is necessary for tightening the parts, and most couplings should be tapped for a set screw.

j. <u>Stand.</u> A stand consists of a base with a pipe socket and an adjustable shaft which will take either a side-stud or a yoke mounting on the instrument. The top of the pipe socket is tapped with a lock handle to hold the instrument at a definite height, generally between 5 and 8 feet. A high stand, 10 to 12 feet, should be mounted on a large base with casters, or a tripod also equipped with casters—this is called a "tower".

k. <u>Stop Collar.</u> A small cast-iron ring fitted on to the adjustable pipe shaft of a regular stand to hold the shaft at a certain height and yet to allow rotation. There is a thumb bolt which always holds it tightly to the shaft, and it rests on the top of the socket of the stand. Used for followspot work.

l. <u>Stud.</u> A threaded 1/2-inch shank projecting from a rotating surface and mounted securely to the side or end of an instrument. Suitable primarily on strip lights.

m. <u>Swing Joint.</u> A 2 or 2 1/2-inch circular surface pierced with a 9/16-inch hole to take a 1/2-inch bolt. Used as a plane of rotation. Usually it is mounted on the top end of the shaft of a stand or at the end of an arm or clamp. Some instruments are equipped with a clutch-tightening mechanism which is very satisfactory.

n. <u>Tower.</u> A fixed or movable high stand or platform on which to mount instruments. The portable type should be equipped with casters and usually has a platform which can be reached by a built-in ladder. On the platform are generally two or three vertical pipes so that a large number of instruments can be mounted in this one place. Towers are made as small as possible, and are apt to be top-heavy, so they should have a means for fastening them to the floor when in place.

o. <u>Tree.</u> A tower with horizontal arms.

p. <u>Washer.</u> Leather for friction joints, iron for use between wing nut and arm to spread the pressure. Split washers prevent the nut from becoming loose, but allow rotation.

q. <u>Yoke.</u> A U-shaped metal piece attached to the sides of the hood with swing joints so that rotation works at the center of gravity of the hood. It must be large enough to allow the hood to swing in a full circle on its axis. Sometimes the arms of the yoke are pierced with two or three holes to allow for close or long coupling. The center of the back is pierced with a hole for taking a 1/2-inch bolt or threaded to take a 1/2-inch pipe. This automatically gives universal rotation and is the most practical mounting accessory to use on spotlights and floods.

2. <u>Types of Mounting</u>

a. <u>Universal Joints.</u> A universal mounting consists of two planes or rotation perpendicular to each other. They need not be directly vertical or horizontal. Depending upon the instrument and extent of universal action, it ought to allow at least a ninety-degree angle of rotation. A leather washer is often used between the planes of rotation to make the joint sticky. An iron washer is used between the nut and the rotating arm to spread the pressure. Split washers prevent the nut from coming loose. A yoke automatically provides universal action. When a pipe clamp and an arm (used for side-stud mounting) are involved, the arm should rotate in the clamp. A knee or elbow arm makes a side-stud mounting automatically universal. With a stand, the rotation of a shaft and a swing joint provides a universal mounting. All spotlights and flood-lights should be allowed universal rotation unless they are mounted to serve for one purpose only.

    b.   Swing Joint. One plane of rotation or perhaps two planes parallel to each other. This is usually found on a striplight mounting where due to its length, only one plane of rotation perpendicular to its length is required. The strip is generally equipped with an end stud attached to the batten by means of an arm with a clamp on one end and a swing joint on the other. A simple swing joint mounting for spotlights, if the arm rotates in the clamp, gives a badly eccentric mounting.

    c.   Chain Hangers. A chain attached to the instrument is wrapped around a horizontal pipe and then hooked to the instrument again. This permits angling strips and floods in one plane of rotation, and has the advantage only of making the instrument come back to its original direction if hit by a piece of scenery or other apparatus.

    d.   Hook Mountings. Bracket lights and backing strips generally are equipped with hooks so that they can be hung on the scenery. This does not permit changing direction. The ordinary picture hook, consisting of a tongue and staple attached to a flat batten, permits quick removal when shifting scenes.

3.   Mounting Methods. The conventional positions for placing instruments generally indicate the types of mounting which are most practical. Many instruments require very careful focusing and may even, as in the case of flood units, have to be moved from scene to scene. The method of mounting should permit this flexibility of position and direction and yet insure rigidity and security.

    a.   Horizontal Batten. For spotlight, yoke, and pipe clamp. The arms of the yoke should be perpendicular unless an eccentric position is necessary, and then the pipe should be fixed. When the pipe is fixed, it is sometimes necessary to use an arm between the yoke and the pipe. This holds true for individual floodlights. Strip lights with end studs use an arm and a pipe clamp or a chain mounting.

    b.   Vertical Batten. Spotlights and floodlights can be clamped directly to the pipe if the yoke is long enough; but where horizontal rotation is necessary from scene to scene, a clamp with a swing joint and an extension arm with two swing joints are necessary. A hook mounting can be had by using a clamp with a swing joint. The hole in the swing joint will accommodate the hook. The vertical batten, used in tormentors for mounting spotlights, must be very accurately placed, because it is difficult to focus the instrument so as to mask it and keep the space small. Generally a flipper is used on the tormentor. When the pipe is mounted two or three inches upstage from the return and about six inches offstage from the joint between the flipper and the return, with an 8-inch arm, it is possible to direct the spotlight either up-stage or across-stage and keep it masked from the sight line. It also requires only a small opening between the upstage edge of the flipper and the downstage end of the set.

    c.   Stands and Towers. Yokes equipped to take the end of the pipe shaft give the most satisfactory noneccentric mounting. Shafts equipped with swing joints are used where the instrument has a side stud. Otherwise, the method is similar to that used on a vertical batten.

    d.   Special Mountings. In addition to the methods described in the previous paragraphs, instruments are used in traps on special legs which serve the purpose of a small stand, or they may be mounted directly on the scenery, as is the case with brackets and backing strips. Every precaution should be made to prevent the hood of the instrument from causing a fire hazard. The mounting should be such that the instrument can be easily cleared during scene shifts. Ceiling fixtures require a special supporting line so that the weight does not hang on the connection. Instruments mounted on the stage floor or on stands should be given adequate space between braces, backings, and other impedimenta backstage.

Occasionally instruments must be manually operated from the space over the stage. In these cases, a portable bridge is necessary. Moving light sources can be mounted on cradles and moved on a track which is hung from the gridiron.

G. WIRING

Modern methods involve the use of portable instruments. In fact, in most traveling professional productions, every piece of equipment is portable so that none of these instruments can be permanently wired to a source of supply. Instruments are equipped with pigtails and male connectors, (the standard "twist lock" connector gives a locked connection preferable to a "pin" connector) or long-run feeds with plugs on the end of them. Each circuit in each instrument is generally fed separately. A pair of asbestos covered wires comes out of the instrument in the form of a pigtail from 12 to 24 inches long, and it is joined to a cable at this point either by permanent splicing or by a male connector which can be connected with a portable piece of cable leading to the outlet box. Inasmuch as most loads are less than 15 amperes it is well to standardize on the No. 14 cable, terminated at one end by a female and the other by a male connector. All pin-connector connections should be tied to take the strain off the connection and to be sure the connection is tight. Ordinary stage plugs provide good spring contact, and have adequate capacity (25 amps.—1/2 plug; 50 amps.—full plug), but they are bulky and require a large receptacle. For a non-traveling producing organization, it seems most practical to have a supply of No. 14 cables in definite lengths, equipped with 15 or 20-ampere connectors on both ends. This presupposes that all stage outlets are of the same type.

1. _Capacities._ No. 14-15 amperes. No. 12-20 amperes. No. 10-25 amperes and No. 8-35 amperes. Pin-connectors and plugs used on the above cables should correspond in capacity.

2. _Types of Cables._

    a. _All rubber, heavy duty._ An extra-flexible, stranded twin-conductor cable with an all-rubber sheath which will stand extremely rough use.

    b. _Fabric-Covered._ An extra-flexible, stranded, twin-conductor cable covered with a double layer of fabric and impregnated with pitch, further strengthened by a pair of hemp cords running the length of it. This type costs about one fourth as much as the first type, but does not stand wear nearly as well.

III. TYPES OF INSTRUMENTS

Instruments are classified broadly as to the type of distribution that they give, although there is considerable overlapping, particularly between the floods and spots. Each classification differs in the type of construction and the degree of control that can be obtained over the four qualities of light. Efficiency is generally sacrificed to obtain control, so that they must always be balanced against each other. The following outline deals with the general characteristics, use, construction, and types of the various instruments. Use can only be discussed in general, inasmuch as every problem may indicate certain special uses. The diversity of construction and the particular type can best be studied in the laboratory. Examples can be found in the numerous equipment catalogs.

A. SPOTLIGHTS

The spotlight might better be called a lens hood, inasmuch as its primary structural feature is the lens. From the standpoint of modeling light, its greatest asset is a control over form, but the efficiency of the standard unit is relatively low. The plano-convex lens unit is considered typical. The characteristics of other variations are considered separately.

1. _History._ The limelight, which consists of an oxyhydrogen flame playing on a stick of lime, was developed in the middle of the last century. This, for the first time, gave an intense white light which could be used successfully with a lens. The arc spot came a little later and rivaled the limelight in its intensity. Both of these, in spite of the fact that they required constant attention, tended to eliminate the complete dependence upon the use of bor-

der lights, footlights, wing strips and floods. They started the practice of front lighting and follow spotting and led to the method of accenting with spotlights and finally to lighting the acting area almost completely by the means of lens units.

The recent development of the efficient fresnel lens unit and the ellipsoidal reflector spotlight practically eliminates the plano-convex spotlight, the arc spot, and in many places the heretofore more efficient projector. However, the standard (or plano-convex lens) spotlight serves as a typical unit and as such deserves considerable attention.

There is still a need for more efficient compact units giving a range of spread, intensity, and color. Eventually, spotlights will be equipped with a remote control of color, beam spread, and direction.

2. Characteristics. Type of light output considered in terms of the four qualities.

    a. Intensity. The spotlight gives an intense beam of light. As the lamp is moved from a position near the focal length toward the lens—from spot to flood focus—the beam intensity decreases (about 10 to 1) in a logarithmic scale, and the total output of light increases accordingly.

    The focal length and the diameter of the lens affect intensity. The larger the lens and the shorter the focal length the greater is the amount of the light output of the lamp gathered by the lens and made useful up to the point where reflection from the incident face of the lens begins to offset the advantage of an increased gathering angle (90°). The rest must be absorbed unless a reflector (good only with pre-focus lamps) is used behind the lamp to send rays, emanating to the rear, back throgh the filament to the lens.

    An efficient spherical reflector increases the output between 25% and 50%, generally about 33%. The efficiency with a large diameter short focal-length lens and a reflector varies between 5% at spot focus and 20% at flood focus; with thin, small diameter lenses between 1% and 10%. See Appendix IV.

    b. Color. The color range depends upon the color mediums used, one at a time, or two or more selective transmissions. Generally a gelatin or plastic film but glass is used in the more permanent installations here.

    c. Distribution. The shape of the beam is conical, generally more intense in the center, and symmetrical about an axis. The image of the filament is liable to show when the lamp is at spot focus.

    For a particular lens and lamp there is a definite relationship between (1) the position of the lamp with regard to the lens, (2) the spread of the beam in degrees, (3) the size of the area lighted, (4) the distance from the area lighted, and (5) the average intensity of illumination falling on the area. If any of the first four are changed, the fifth changes in a logarithmic progression: brighter when the lamp is moved away from the lens, and vice versa.

    The edge of the beam is relatively hard unless softened by diffusers. These cause a spill of light which may require the use of funnels. Cutoffs are a means of limiting or shaping the beam. The spotlight causes a single sharp shadow, dependent upon the direction of light rays in relation to the position of the object lighted.

    d. Movement. Dimming the source gives a complete range of intensity, from the maximum brightness of the lamp in use, to out, or vice versa. Many spotlights are adaptable to several sizes of lamps for a change in intensity. A color wheel, a remote boomerang control, or the changing of the color frame by hand gives variety in color, but the line of change is apt to show. Different focal-length lenses give a variety in range of spread.

Although the position of the instrument is generally fixed, the direction is adjustable for use as follow spot or can be changed from scene to scene through a universal joint mounting usually manually, but sometimes remotely by mechanical electrical control. The spread is adjustable by changing the position of the lamp in relation to the lens, or by changing the shape of the beam by flippers, shutters, and mats.

3. Genertal Use.

   a. To obtain a localized intensity desired on a definite area or object.

   b. To obtain an intense color or special tint on a particular object.

   c. To light the acting areas separately from the background.

   d. To give emphasis to essential detail.

   e. To spotlight. Danger of spotty effect and over-emphasis, due to hard edge and contrast.

   f. To obtain plasticity and create high light, shade and shadow.

4. Construction. A well-ventilated metal hood equipped with converging lens of moderate focal length and a concentrated filament light source. The hood is equipped with an access door, a color-frame slide, an adjustable focus slide on which the socket of the lamp is mounted, and a mounting apparatus.

   a. The Light Source. (See Chapter 1) A concentrated filament G or T-shape lamp; arc burners for arc spots.

      The size of the bulb determines somewhat the width, the height of the hood. A screw base for all barrel filament mountings (C-5) and a prefocus or bipost base for all mono-plane and biplane filament forms (C-13 and C-13D). There is an external manual adjustment for arc burners to keep the crater on an axis with the center of the lens.

   b. Focal Slide. This carries the socket of the lamp (either medium or mogul, which may be adjustable as to height to place the filament center on the axis of the lens), and sometimes a spherical concave reflector. The slide moves the socket from a position close to the lens (so that the bulb comes within 1/4 to 1/2 inch) to a point just short of the focal length. Spill light through the slot in the base of the hood should be eliminated by baffles. A thumb bolt or worm gear is provided to move the slide and to hold it in position.

      The range of beam spread is determined by the length of the slot and the focal length of the lens. This more or less determines the length of the hood. Socket adapters and socket extensions allow for the use of various sizes of lamps.

   c. Reflector. (See section on Accessories.) A polished metal, concave spherical reflector mounted on the focal slide on the axis of the lens behind the lamp (1/2 to 1 inch from the bulb) so that its center of curvature coincides with the lamp filament. The position may be adjustable. If it is out of position it gives a secondary beam of light, and is therefore often removed by operators or not included by manufacturers. It should be large enough to redirect rays to the entire lens at flood position.

   d. Lens. (See Accessories.) A round converging lens, mounted in front of the hood by means of a spring ring or clamps. It should be loose enough to allow for expansion under heat. Special lenses, such as step, meniscus, or tubular can be used to obtain special distributions. See Fresnel spot below.

   e. Hood. Ruggedly built, and riveted, of 20-gage metal. Inside painted dead black so that there will be no reflected light. Equipped with an access door for the easy removal of the lamp in case it burns out. Thoroughly ventilated by covered vents which allow no light spill. Its size is determined chiefly by the size of the lamp, the length of the focal slide, and the size of the lens.

f. Color-Frame Slides. Attached to the front of the hood, often horizontal, large enough to accommodate at least two color frames, cutoff apparatus, or effects; usually equipped with a spring or lock bolt to hold the frames in place. Generally the slides should be vertical with a bottom stop. The slide mounting should permit rotation when the instrument is tipped to one side or the other. Omitted where there is remote control of the color medium. Need for standardized sizes.

g. Mounting Apparatus. (See Accessories.) Generally side stud or yoke. Equipped with an arm or pipe clamp or both. Stands and bases.

h. Wiring. (See Accessories.) Two individual leads of asbestos-covered wire, connected to the socket at covered terminals, emerging from bottom or rear of hood through two bushed openings. Equipped with a 18" to 36" asbestos pigtail of sufficient capacity (5, 15, 30, Amp.) or a long length of cable terminated by a male plug, a pin-connector or a twist lock plug. Lead-in wires should be clamped in position or knotted inside the hood with sufficient slack to allow for focal adjustment. German instruments have a connector equipped with latch mounted on the instrument to hold the feed connector in tight contact.

5. Types. (See Appendix IV)

a. Plano-convex Spot. Baby spot—250 and 400-watt G-30 barrel filament lamp with 4 1/2 to 5" lenses. Regular spot—1000, 1500, and 2000-watt G-40 lamp with 6 x 8, 9, or 10, 12, or 14" lenses. Generally no reflector. Arc 70-150 Amps.

b. Fresnel Spot. 3"—100-watt G-16 1/4 monoplane filament lamp. 6"—250, 500 or 750-watt T-20, mono- and biplane filament lamp. 8"—1000 and 1500-watt G-40 biplane filament lamp. 10" and 12"—2000-watt G-48 biplane prefocus or bipost lamp. 14" or 16" and 20" for 5000 and 10,000-watt lamps respectively. All sizes use a spherical reflector.

The characteristics of this type are the same as those of the plano-convex lens unit except that the short-focal-length lens gathers so much more light that the efficiency, and therefore the relative brightness, is from two to four times as great.

The flutes and diffusing dimples (on the rear) of the lens give a soft edge to the beam and thus preclude its use where spill light is objectionable unless a long funnel is attached.

The beam spread can be varied from approximately 15 to 50 degrees. Generally only one focal length in each diameter of lens is obtainable. It is roughly about half the diameter, and made of heat-resisting glass. The hood is short, with access through the top or front. Mounting apparatus—a yoke.

c. Ellipsoidal Reflector Spot. 4 1/2"—250-watt T-12, monoplane, and 500-watt T-12 biplane filament lamp; wide-angle (45°) beam. 6" up to 750-watt, longer hood, medium beam (30°). Long 8" lens hood, narrow beam (15°) up to 1000-watt units. Larger reflectors and hoods are made for 10" 750 and 1000-watt T-12 biplane filament lamps (12°). 12" follow spot unit with a 10° beam using a 3000-watt T-32 lamp. A 2100 W 60 volt lamp with a 16" lens gives 2,000,000 beam candle power in an 8° beam. The characteristics of these units while similar to the spotlight in effect, in construction are so different they must be classified as a distinct type.

The wide angle unit gives the greatest output (per watt) but the narrow beam the greatest beam candle power. There is no lamp focusing except to adjust the filament so that it lies at the optical center of the reflector.

32

The beam of light has an intense center and is shaped by the shutter or gate or iris from its maximum spread to zero with a relatively sharp edge or cutoff, depending upon the in-and-out focus position of the lens. The intensity of light in any part of the beam does not change perceptibly with the movement of the shutters or iris and very slightly when the lens is moved.

In view of these characteristics, this unit makes an ideal front spot particularly where a sharp cutoff is desired. Its efficiency makes it useful for long throws and follow spotting. By throwing the lens out of focus, it can be made soft edged to a limited degree.

Of the various structural parts, the reflector is the most important. It consists roughly of a spun Alzak half elipsoid with the major axis short, and the diameter large for a wide beam; the opposite for a narrow beam. In small sizes it is now made with annular flats to give a smoother field.

The lamp burns base up (mounted at a slight angle sloping backwards because the hood is generally focused downward when in use). The plane or planes of the filament are parallel to the axis of the reflector and mounted at the focal point of the reflector. As the rays strike the reflector, they are reflected so that they pass through the conjugate focal point. At this point the rays form a concentration in cross section several times the area of the filament and then proceed until they strike the lens.

The shutter or gate is located just short of the concentration point. It has vertical and horizontal cutoffs (four way) which can be tipped to give an irregular shape to the beam. A template with a predetermined shape cut in it may also be used. For follow-spot work an iris is generally used in place of the four-way cutoffs.

The lens must be of a medium to short focal length (less than the distance from the gate to the lens) so that it can perform two functions. One to focus the shape of the gate sharply on the area lighted and the other to determine the spread of the beam. It acts as an objective lens system, and may consist of one or two plano-convex lenses, or a step lens. The lens is mounted in a carrier which permits moving it forward or backward one or two inches, to throw the beam edge in or out of focus.

The hood is longer than the regular spotlight. Access to the lamp generally is had by removing the socket mounting.

   d.   Spot and Floodlight Reflector Lamps. See discussion of Reflector Lamp, Chapter 1.

B. FLOODLIGHTS

Floodlights are intermediate instruments between spotlights and strips. They provide relatively little control of the light, and the rays that emerge directly from the filament are usually at odds with the reflected rays. Efficiency is relatively high, inasmuch as most of the rays of the total emanation are used.

1. History. Floodlights were developed from the limelight and the arc lights, and were used for giving general localized lighting to entrances and special pieces of scenery at close range. With the advent of the incandescent lamp, the first type consisted of an open-faced hood with a "bunch" of small lamps, and later a large single high-powered lamp mounted in a hood with a V-shaped back, called an Olivette. These have almost been superseded by the more efficient ellipsoidal reflector with an etched aluminum reflecting surface.

The projector, using a high-powered lamp and a parabolic reflector, was long used to floodlight buildings before it found its way into the theatre. It is simply a form of searchlight which comes down to us from long in the past. But, now, with the greater efficiency of the projector over the spotlight minimized because of the development of the fresnel spot, the advantage of using the projector no longer exists, and its bulkiness may soon be reason enough for its elimination from the stage.

There is still some use for an open-face flood which will give a concentrated or spread distribution in various intensities and an even illumination over an area without showing a sharp edge. These should be compact and provide a complete range of color. The reflector lamp now appearing in various sizes and spreads is meeting this need more and more.

2. Characteristics.

 a. Intensity. Intensity is more or less proportional to the wattage of the lamp. The output is dependent upon the gathering power of the reflector, its coefficient of reflection, and amount of direct emanation used.

 b. Color. The color range is the same as in a spotlight, except that with ellipsoidal and parabolic units, colors can be changed almost without showing a distinct line.

 c. Distribution. The distribution is a broad spread of light, although projectors using parabolic reflectors give an efficient narrow beam of light. The searchlight and automobile headlight are examples. The distribution is generally symmetrical about an axis. There is apt to be a hard edge to the lighted area due to direct emanation, except when the reflector surface is diffusing. Intensity is inversely proportional to range of spread—from 5 to 30 degrees in projectors, up to 180 degrees with ordinary floodlights. A broad area is lighted, but intensity falls off quickly as distance increases. Single, relatively soft-edged shadow, due to the size of the face of the instrument. Diffusing mediums.

 d. Movement. Projectors are adaptable to only a few sizes of lamps and have a limited focal range. Shaped polished reflectors generally can accommodate only one size of lamp, because of their fixed focal length. Diffusing reflector with white surface such as the Olivette, take any size of lamp up to 2000 watts.

3. Use

 a. Floodlights are generally used to illuminate broad surfaces at close range, at relatively low intensity.

 b. Banks or rows which approximate strip lights give high-powered general light over broad surfaces and allow more or less the same range of color control as in strip lights. Remote color control effective.

 c. Used for general localized illumination at entrances or for broad acting areas. Give more or less the same effect of light and shade as spotlights with less intensity. Projectors are used to simulate sunlight and moonlight, and for long throws. Soft edge. Filament images.

4. Construction. A well-ventilated open-faced metal hood with interior reflecting surface and some kind of high powered single light source, or bunch of small lamps.

 a. Light Source. T-20, 250, 500, and 750 for 10" and G-type lamps of 500, 1000 and 1500-watts are used in 16" projectors. General floods use the P. S.-type lamp, generally mounted base up. All sizes from 25-watts to 10, 000. (500-1000-watts, usual range. Sometimes a G-30 250 or 400-watt).

 b. Focal arrangement. Generally used with the G-type lamp in parabolic reflectors only. When the projector is to be directed down at an angle greater than 45 degrees, a socket must be mounted in front of the instrument, or any way so that the lamp burns most nearly base down.

 Only a slight adjustment in the focal slide is necessary—beyond the focal length causes a crossing of the rays with a hole in the center of the beam, inside the focal length, a spreading. Worm adjustment.

c. **Reflector.** Projectors use a reflector of polished metal of a simple or compound parabolic shape. The size is dependent upon its focal length, the dimensions of the bulb, the practical limits of the overall bulk of the instrument, and the amount of direct emanation to be gathered. Ellipsoidal reflectors generally give a spread reflection and have an etched aluminum surface. Olivette; flat white surface and v-shaped back.

d. **Hood.** Large open-faced, well-braced or spun-metal shape, made of at least twenty-gage metal. Adequate ventilation, although not as essential as in a spotlight. The heat radiates from aluminum hoods.

e. **Color-Frame Side or Grooves.** Generally similar to spotlight. Should be vertical with a bottom stop. Larger than face of the hood. Color frame clipped on in some large units.

f. **Mounting.** Generally yoke or stud mounting for use on a stand or horizontal batten. Some chain mounting used for battens, but the best is the yoke-and-pipe-clamp type.

g. **Wiring.** In a focusing instrument, the wiring is generally similar to a spotlight. Otherwise a cable comes out through a single, bushed opening.

h. **Accessories.** Projectors—concentric or sleeve louvers, a spherical front reflector, or step lens to control direct emanation. Color frames, generally of large size with cross wires to hold gelatin. Wooden 18" by 20" frames used for Olivettes. Cutoffs are useless on the average flood.

5. **Types.** The two general types are projectors and general floods. Each reflector in a compartment strip is a small floodlight. The term previously applied to the Olivette or bunch light, but recent developments have brought out a more efficient type of flood using ellipsoidal or small parabolic shapes with etched aluminum surface to give more general control over the spread.

   a. **Projectors.** 200 to 10,000-watt G-type lamps, used to give 8 to 20 degrees of spread. P.S. lamps give from 15 to 30 degrees spread. A silvered glass, chromium or alzak parabolic reflector.

   b. **General Floods.** 100 to 2000-watt lamps. Olivette 1000 to 2000-P.S. Etched 14" and 18" aluminum ellipsoidal shapes. 500 to 2000-watt P.S. (10" with the base down will take a 250 or 400-watt G-type lamp.)

   c. **Flood Light Lamp.** See discussion of Reflector Lamp, Chapter 1.

C. STRIP LIGHTS

Strip lights allow the least control of the form of light and thus have relatively high efficiency. They are the only units in which a complete range of color can be obtained according to present practice. They consist of a row of similar sources; ideally, a line of light. They are made in many forms to serve any purpose where there is a need for general shadowless illumination and a range of color.

1. **History.** Strip lights were derived from the conventional rows of candle, oil and gaslight sources used behind borders and wings.

   With the development of the electric lamp they consisted of a single or double row of small sources in different colors placed in an open-faced reflector, closely together, giving low, general, shadowless illumination. These strips were often divided into sections for control and dipped lamps supplied the color.

   About 1918, the theatre borrowed the efficient store-window reflector strips which had been given a trade name of X-ray, and almost instantly all border lights became known as X-rays. These individual reflectors permitted the use of larger-size lamps and more recently a compact compound parabolic metal reflector has been developed which controls the light even more efficiently.

2. **Characteristics.**

   a. Intensity. Low-intensity distribution generally, although larger wattages can give the intensity of a row of floods. The efficiency is equal to that of a floodlight, but the intensity does not represent wattage involved, inasmuch as all lights are seldom burned at the same time. Two or more of the circuits may be on dimmer reading to give a color tone.

   b. Color. Complete color range by using the three primary colors or any tints desired. A fourth color, white or amber, is a practical addition to give tints and intensity.

   c. Distribution. Relatively shadowless in effect, provided there are more than ten similar color units burning and the object is perpendicular to the line of light. The additive result is the distribution of each source taken in a line. Distribution broad, parallel to the row of light sources, and of a thickness equal to the distribution from one source; on the other axis, narrow with polished parabolic reflectors, medium with etched aluminum, and wide with etched aluminum in an ellipsoidal shape.

   d. Movement. Color can be varied by dimming on and off the color circuits. Distribution can be varied by separate control of the various sections.

3. **Use.**

   a. Footlights to tone the setting and illuminate shadows.

   b. X-ray strips or border lights give general illumination for the scenery—borders and backdrops and cycloramas.

   c. Horizon or "cyc" foots to give illumination in any color to the base of a cyclorama or dome.

   d. Cyc overhead in short sections following curve of cyc at some distance.

   e. Strips on the floor to illuminate ground rows.

4. **Construction.** Any row of individual light sources or several light sources fixed in a line in a continuous or compartment reflecting hood. Generally consisting of a row of medium base receptacles, closely spaced, wired in one, three, or four circuits and sometimes split into several sections for the sake of control or portability. Double rows sometimes used to increase intensity and to save space.

5. **Types.**

   a. Footlights. A compact strip, mounted in a pit in the front of the stage. It should approximate a line of light in any color and be hooded so that the distribution falls within the proscenium and illuminates the set evenly. The hood should not be over 3" above floor line.

   Light sources range from 25 to 200-watts P. S.; natural colored or dipped lamps up to 40-watts, in a continuous open strip. 60, 100, 150, and 200 watts in compartment form. Part of the filament above the floor. Lamp mounted with end facing stage. Color mediums used with the compartment type. Glass roundels or gelatin. Natural color or dipped lamps up to 40 watts in open-faced units. Reflectors consist of a cylindrically curved flat-white or metallic surface—in the open-faced type—or of individual ellipsoidal-parabolic shapes giving regular or spread reflection. The strip is built as a continuous metal hood with a white surface or as a single or double row of sockets or small reflectors. Five to ten feet shorter than the width of the proscenium opening. Built in sections and mounted permanently in the footlight trough or mounted in portable or disappearing sections. Disappearing type has disconnect switches to open circuits when closed. Wiring—one, three, or four colors, and in sections. Permanent wiring for fixed strips. Pigtails for portable units, with connectors on each end of each section. Center section of three longer than the combined length of the end sections. Outlets to feed footlight spots.

b. Borderlights (X-Rays). Borderlights are the strips used over the stage. They are generally wired for three color circuits. Usually the first border is controlled in two or three sections. It hangs over the stage just behind the teaser and is often as long as the width of the proscenium opening. It is sometimes called the concert border, but generally simply "X-rays". Other borders are ranged conventionally on seven foot centers going toward the back of the stage. The rear border is generally of high wattage for lighting cycloramas or backdrops. Border battens are now often equipped only with outlets so that portable strips, spots or floods can be connected at these positions. The close spacing of similarly colored units is important only where the border hangs near to the surface to be lighted.

Light sources 60, 100, 150, 300, 500, and even 1000-watt P.S. lamps, 200-watt normal for conventional stage. Reflector lamps, spotlight for high, flood light for low teasers in the 150- and 300-watt sizes are being used more every day because they are efficient and compact, but hard on gelatin.

Reflectors are shaped to direct the light down on the stage. The compartment style, a row of small floods with shaped reflectors of etched aluminum, alzak, or chromium finish. Narrow beam for high mounting, medium for average, and wide-angle for low prosceniums. Equipped with color-frame slides or glass roundels.

Mounting—the continuous strip is hung by clamps (generally to a movable-pipe batten) or chains which permit a certain amount of rotation to allow for whatever bumping might occur in flying the scenery. Sectional compartment strips, portable type mounting obtained by means of the end stud, swing-joint, arm, and pipe-clamp assembly which permits definite direction and eccentric hanging, particularly under the bridge.

Borders are wired in one, three, or four color circuits and often divided in sections. In fixed strips fed by multi-conductor cable supported from the grid or side wall. When several sections are used together, each section has a set of male pigtails at one end and female at the other. Connections made to outlets on pipe battens or bridge. Permanent strips often include a separate work-light circuit.

c. Cyclorama Lights. Cyclorama borders are made up of single or multiple rows of high-powered floodlights or strips. 200, 300, and 500-watt P.S. lamps generally wired for three colors. Circuits sometimes controlled in sections. Cyclorama lights should distribute a general even light over the surface of the cyclorama and tend to eliminate the shadows of any wrinkles or unevenness in the surface. The best position is well downstage from the surface to be lighted. However, to obtain this the fly space must be clear of hanging scenery. Where free fly space is necessary, concentrating reflector or reflector-lamp strips should be used close to the top of the cyclorama

d. Horizon Lights, or "Cyc Foots". High-powered strips used at the base of the cyclorama or dome. P.S. or reflector lamps sometimes in two rows. Generally the primary colors used here, to allow complete changes of horizon effects on background— for example, sunsets. 150, 200, or 300-watt lamps. Wattage may compensate for difference in transmission of various colors, roughly on the basis of one for green, two for red, three for blue, and one-half for white, or amber if used. Reflectors, concentrating or having a lateral spread for mixing. Equipped with color frames or glass roundels. Mounted in the pit or on the floor in sections, but sufficiently far from the bottom of the cyclorama or dome to allow complete color mixing from units of similar colors. Projector spotlight lamp strips (no reflectors) with spread roundels give a high-powered sheet of light from close range. Those set on the floor should be mounted on trucks. Should have an adjustable plane of rotation. Often wired for control in center and end sections. Portable strips equipped with pigtails and connectors on both ends for feed-through. Light pit when used with flying cyclorama should be able to be covered quickly.

e. **Portable Strips.** In one or several colors, used for lighting entrances or ground rows with a general distribution. Small wattage lamps up to 200-watts, generally not above 100. Use dipped or natural color lamps, color frames or glass roundels. Wired in three or four colors. Equipped with chain or end stud for mounting. Reflector similar to open trough or row of individual concentrating types. Very narrow strips use T-type lamps.

f. **Backing Strips.** One circuit of four to twelve small wattage lamps, 25-100. Each mounted parallel to the direction of the strip in small compartments. Equipped with a hook for mounting. Used for lighting entrances.

g. **Side Silvered Lamps.** See discussion of Reflector Lamp, Chapter 1.

D. SPECIAL INSTRUMENTS

1. **History.** Many instruments developed in the last century were used to give the effects of fire, moving clouds, rippling water, and abstract moving patterns. These were an elaboration of the magic lantern, and they achieved an instant popularity, probably because of their novelty. The motion picture projector is a form of this same principle. Another instrument, called the shadow projector or Linnebach lantern, borrowed the simple principle of the Javanese shadow play, and made it possible to project whole scenes from one light source. The German cloud machine, developed about 1910, is an elaborate optical apparatus for projecting pictures of actual clouds and moving them across the cyclorama in a very realistic manner.

The Germans have also been instrumental in developing all kinds of projected scenery, but it has not found much use in this country. In 1921 Wilfred's Clavilux caused considerable interest. It projected abstract moving patterns on the screen and suggested the possibility of light as an art form of expression, or the enhancement of music by the contribution of visual effects.

2. **Linnebach Lantern.**

a. **Use.** To project large patterns at close range by direct emanation from a concentrated light source. Shadow projections. Requires a broad screen or a translucency if used from behind.

b. **Characteristics.** A broad area (up to generally about 60° x 90°) covered with a simple pattern. The details of the slide must be larger than the filament of the light source. Penumbra effect. Edges blurred. No focus. Distortion great unless the slide is parallel to the screen. Irregular intensity. Vibrant image apt to be distracting. With two or more incandescent units, one can be dimmed off and another dimmed on. Thus one backdrop can serve to give the effect of any number of scenes.

c. **Construction.** A high-powered concentrated light source (1500-3000 w. filament, or a carbon arc) mounted in a funnel-shaped hood with a flat black inside. A spherical reflector can be used back of the filament source if perfectly centered. The front of the hood consists of a large rectangular opening with grooves for the slide. The slide is made of glass with a transparent pattern painted on it or of gelatin and an opaque perforated mat. The instrument is generally mounted on the floor back of a translucency, or hung overhead in front of an opaque drop or cyc.

3. **Effect Machine.** A means of projecting precisely, at a large scale, the details of a slide on any receiving surface.

a.   Use. These may be either static or moving patterns of light on the background, such as clouds, landscapes, rain, fire and may even serve in the place of painting on the scenery itself. In Germany and Austria experiments have been made in profecting the two-dimensional details of painted scenery on white flats. In a box-set form these flats can give the impression of any number of scenes, merely by changing the slides in the effect machine. See catalogs for the variety of effects available.

b.   Characteristics. Effects are vibrant and colorful beyond any brightness that is usually given by pigment. They are limited as to spread up to 60 degrees, but the smaller the angle the sharper the image, and the image may be irregular unless distortion is allowed for in making the slide.

Distortion results from angular projection and presents the greatest problem in using effects because the instrument can seldom be directed straight at the screen. By a laborious trial and error method, by taking a photograph of a model of the finished effect, by a careful application of the formulas to get precise dimensions, or by tipping the slide so that it is angled to the screen, distortion can be minimized. But at extreme angles (30° to 45°) only the last will give an image that is reasonably sharp at the edges. The center is generally brighter than the edges.

Any jarring of the effect machine or screen discloses the nature of the projection.

Excessive movement in the projection is apt to be distracting.

c.   Construction. Effect machine consists of:

   (1)   a high powered light source in a spotlight; 1500 to 5000 watts or an arc.

   (2)   extra condensing lens, the "dutchman", or lenses to converge the rays on the slide.

   (3)   a water jacket for cooling is recommended with an arc source.

   (4)   an effect head or drum or slide; and

   (5)   an objective.

The light source used at the approximate focal length of the spotlight lens (short focal length), sends out parallel rays of light to the second condenser, which in turn causes the rays to pass through the slide and converge on the center of the objective. (Condenser lenses are plano-convex lenses mounted so that the curved surfaces face each other to avoid spherical and chromatic aberration).

The slide or object is smaller than the condenser system, and at a definite distance from the objective, it is inverted, and must be very accurately made. Photographs are useful, as every detail is exaggerated in the image.

The image or projected pattern can be softened by throwing the objective out of focus. Distortion and irregular intensity of the image result when effect machine is used at an angle to the screen.

The objective is smaller in diameter than the slide; large for short focal-lengths, small for long focal-lengths. In its cheapest form it consists of two converging plano convex lenses mounted in a tube which can be adjusted in relation to the slide. Also in some cases the two lenses of the objective are adjustable in relation to each other to offer a range of objective focal length.

When P is the dimension of the object; p is the distance of the object to the center of the objective; Q is the dimension of the image; q is the distance between the instrument and the image; and f is the focal length of the objective, then

$$\frac{1}{p} + \frac{1}{q} = \frac{1}{f} \qquad \frac{P}{Q} = \frac{P}{q}.$$

Also when f_2 is the focal length of the first lens in the objective; f is the focal length of the second lens (their round surfaces facing each other); and d is the distance between the two, then

$$f = \frac{f_1 \times f_2}{f_1 + f_2 - d}.$$

Effect machines can be mounted on a stand, either on the floor, on a bridge, behind backdrops or cycloramas, on a tower on the side of the stage; in the face of the balcony, the projection booth, or the ceiling beams.

A framing shutter is required usually to give a rectangular cutoff to the image. Effects are generally hand painted, operated by clockworks of variable speed or by motor.

    d.   Types.   The ordinary slide-projection machine is for static images.

Water Ripple. Several moving slides of strips of glass set on edge toward the light source with a diffuser.

Moving Effects painted on mica discs. Double discs used for movement within movement such as fire and moving panoramas.

German cloud-effect machine uses several projectors with photographs of clouds, revolving about a single light source. The image is projected upon a mirror which can be controlled in direction, thus permitting overlapping and multiple movement among the various cloud images.

4.   Lightning Effects. Produced by striking two electrodes of an arc together, mounted in an open hood protected by a screen guard. Can be colored and gives general effect of sharp flood of bright light. Operated by press button, equipped with a rheostat, and generally used in the wings or from the bridge.

Lightning can also be obtained by flashing projected storm clouds or by a static slide with a picture of lightning on it.

Generally a flash of the border lights, footlights, or a floodlight is adequate.

5.   Onstage Fixtures. Wall brackets, chandeliers, table lamps, etc. Used as motivating sources. Should be well shielded and house small wattage lamps. Only a glow is desired. If a large light source is well shielded so that it is not in the line of vision, it can be used as an illuminating source. Generally the fixture becomes too bulky to be decorative. Fixtures should be rigidly supported and not hung on feed cable. Connections are made behind setting. Use of bushing where cable passes through the scenery. Support for cable. Fixtures must be portable so that they can be struck quickly. Tongue and staple mounting for brackets.

6.   Fires. Convincing flames are very difficult to produce. Colored silk banners fluttered by a fan and illuminated by red and amber lamps mounted below. Fire logs, built to be partially transparent, housing red and amber lamps, one, two or three circuits of which can be varied in intensity. Rotors: vane-topped transparent cylinders operated by the heat of a lamp, two rotating in opposite directions. Used effectively in coal grates. Coal can be simulated by broken glass, partially painted out with lamp black. Artificial smoke.

IV. DESIGN OF INSTRUMENTS

The perfect instrument should allow for the creation and control of the four qualities of light, intensity, color, form and movement, within certain limits. Mechanical and technical limitations determined by the structural arrangements of the space to be lighted, and choice of available equipment, naturally make any lighting somewhat arbitrary or conventionalized. The designer should be able to design or select instruments which, due to their flexibility of control, do not tend to limit the final effect.

A. GENERAL SPECIFICATIONS

The use of the electric lamp, advantageous as it is over the old sources of illumination, involves definite mechanical, optical and electrical features in the design of the instruments. If the principles governing the design are kept in mind so that the efficient control of all the qualities of light is held as the goal, the practical variable will determine the extent to which each instrument can approach this ideal.

Traditional practice, limited demand, stock production, and the ignorance of scientific principles have tended to retard the development of the most practical instruments for use on the stage. Instruments are designed to satisfy a number of requirements so that they should be selected from stock, based on their practical ability to satisfy the following conditions.

1. Adaptability. Flexibility in the range of light distribution and its control is dependent upon the uses required of the instrument. It should be selected generally to serve from one position throughout the play and yet be accessible; to have wattage sufficient to supply the greatest brightness in view of the changes in color, focus and direction. Some instruments such as footlights, X-ray borders, and horizon strips, such as are designed to give a special distribution, are more practical if used in their specific positions than when limited in design in order to be adapted to serve in a number of different positions. Light sources should be selected as to wattage, shape, and color that will give a range of adaptability.

2. Efficiency. The lumen output per watt consumed is of relative importance. In order to obtain a balance of distribution in several instruments, each light source is almost always on dimmer reading to some degree. Accessories, such as color mediums, lenses, reflectors, and cutoffs, limit efficiency for the sake of control.

3. Simplicity, Dependability and Weight. Instruments should be easy to operate and to mount, strong to withstand rough usage. The size of parts and weight are important, and they should be of stock material and sizes which can easily be replaced. Adequate protection and accessibility to lamp. Portability. Universal joints. Sticky joints.

4. Heating Effect. Ventilation should be adequate to prolong the life of the lamp and the color medium and to avoid fire hazard. Four times as much ventilation in top as in bottom. Asbestos insulation. Guards. No inflammable parts.

5. Code and Safety. The law determines the general construction and type of accessories that can be employed in the manufacture and use of electrical apparatus. Safety and strength to provide against injury to the operator and bystander or the layout. 20-gage metal, soldered connections in strips.

6. Cost. Stock equipment designed by a reputable firm to satisfy the above conditions is always more economical than special instruments, except as the latter have continued use and are better suited to the purpose than anything obtainable in stock. An extended demand creates a practical market for the manufacturing company. However, cheapness in the cost of lighting equipment is never a cirterion of worth. Instruments should be given a trial or their characteristics understood before purchase.

7. Effect. The performance of an instrument is its ultimate criterion of worth. The amount of light, its color, smoothness of field and sharpness or softness of edge (whichever is important) are comparative standards upon which the value of an instrument as a lighting tool can be based.

3. CONTROL

The lighting of a production directs and focuses the attention of the audience, composes and unifies the stage picture, orients the audience in time and place, provides the mood of the scene and of the play, and provides visibility. If the lighting designer proposes to achieve a fulfillment of these functions, he must require a high degree of control over the stage lighting sources. In order to communicate his design sense and feeling to the audience, the designer may use electrical, mechanical, and optical means to control the medium of light. As a means of design expression, control is considered as one of the most important aspects of stage lighting.

Although the immediate concern of a lighting designer is the development and execution of the lighting for a particular production, other factors influence and modify his concept: the director's approach, the scenic designer's concept, the playwright's intent, and the more mundane and realistic factors of production budget, available equipment and personnel, and the geometry of the stage. After the artistic direction has been established and all of the component parts of the production integrated and balanced, they must be given a vitality: no matter how appealing, a static stage picture will not hold an audience's attention. The elements of the production must interact and move with a refined and heightened dynamic sense. The playwright can write, the director can direct, and the actor can act; unless their stage environment moves and acts with them, the audience will sense an incompleteness. It is the duty of lighting to provide a focal point for the stage picture. Since the focal point must change as the physical and psychological interaction changes, the lights must change. Such a change in lighting direction, focus, mood, and picture must not detract from the stage action; such a change must be subtle and sensitive. The lighting control system must allow the lighting designer to acheive such movement and control.

In some instances lighting is expected to contribute only visibility and a limited range of naturalistic effects, such as changes of time of day, moonlight, lightning, etc. As more and more producers and directors experience the compositional and modal uses of light, they awaken to the enhancement such lighting can contribute to their own productions. Modern lighting systems can provide such expression; it is the job of the lighting designer and stage electrician to understand and exploit the greater freedom and ease of control such systems allow.

Ideally, the stage lighting should be under the control of one person who creates lighting as an organist creates music: his score, the cue sheet; his playing, the operation of the control board. Light is a visual sensation, as music is an auditory sensation. If the operator of such a light "organ" can not experience the visual effects he is producing, his operations will be as uneffective as those of an organist who can not sense the music he is playing. (The number of available Beethovens of stage lighting is limited). Good lighting has been produced by operators who are unable to see the stage; for such lighting to be accomplished, the artistry and feeling of the designer must be translated into the routined mechanics of, for example:

> "get ready for blackout; 2, 5, 8, 9, 11, 12, sneak them on
> interlock (quiet scene, can't have any noise) o.k.; pull 1, 3,
> 5, after blackout; take the master down on cue with a 5 count;
> after 2 count, start 1 and 3 down; they should be at about two
> by the time the blackout cue comes. Seems longer tonight;
> wonder if he forgot to throw the cue---no; Tom always exits
> first. o.k., there's Tom, get ready---which was it? 1 and 3.
> Cue, easy down, one one-thousand, two one-thousand, start
> one and three, four one-thousand, counting too slow, there's
> Lisa now; master out, move a little faster. About there,
> o.k. cue, pull the switch. Good. Unlock 5, 9, 11, lock 7 and
> 10 on. o.k., kill 1, 3, 5, o.k., Cue, bump-up, good, o.k.,
> follow with 9 and 11 twelve count, one one-thousand, two one-
> thousand . . ."

The mind of the operator under such adverse control conditions can not concentrate on what is actually happening on stage; his understanding of the lighting concept is in cues and counts. Sensitive and dynamic control of stage lighting depends on both the operator's technical skill and his intellectual understanding of the art.

The purpose for which lighting is to be used dictates the extent to which control should be provided: a lighting designer who would specify a 60 circuit remote control electronic infinite preset system for the speakers' platform of a meeting room would be out of a job as quickly as a lighting designer who would require only two 5 amp single pole single throw toggle switches to control the lighting for a complete production of Wagner's Ring Cycle. In between these extremes there are many ordinary situations which require a lighting designer to call for a control system to suit a particular production, a particular repertory, or a particular stage. In order to arrive at an intelligent decision, the lighting designer or stage electrician must understand the nature of control; the techniques, terminology, and technology of control; control system availability, and cost; and the basic principles of control design.

I. THE NATURE OF CONTROL

Lighting control is accomplished by regulation of the qualities of light to produce the desired dramatic effect. From the study of instruments it is apparent that a range of the qualities of light can be achieved by optical, mechanical, and electrical means. Since we are able to gain a wide range of control over the other qualities of light, through the electrical control of intensity, this approach appears to be the simplest and most flexible; presently, this is the most satisfactory and practical approach.

The effect of control on the qualities of light and, ultimately, the production, is determined by a balancing and interaction of the effect of each instrument. As the composer of an orchestral symphony scores the playing for various groups of instruments to achieve the desired auditory effect, so must the lighting designer arrange his lighting to achieve the desired visual effect through the selection of lighting instruments; as the conductor of an orchestra synchronizes and controls the playing of the score, so must the lighting control operator synchronize and control the performance of lighting cues. The symphony which we expect in the ultimate use of light depends on the subtle arrangement and sequencing of a number of instruments, each selected to provide a particular effect in harmony with the desired total effect.

A. INTENSITY

Generally the wattage of the light source determines the maximum lumen output of each instrument. In turn, the instrument determines the proportion of the lumen output that is effective, and the additive effect of all the light rays striking an object determines the intensity of light illuminating the object. The brightness of the object finally determines the amount of light that reaches the eye of an observer. A change in any one of these factors influences the effect of intensity, and may be used to control light intensity. However, it is more practical to control the output of the source by reducing or increasing the electrical power available to the source, rather than controlling optical or mechanical devices between the source and the lighted object.

B. COLOR

The color of the light, usually originating from a white-light source, depends on the selective transmission of color media placed between the source and the lighted object. The additive effect of all light striking the object, and the selective color reflection of the object, determine the final color effect. Presently, the most practical means of color control is by intensity variation in two or more light sources (each source having a different color filter). The three primary colors used in strip lights permit remote control of color in any tint or shade by varying the settings of three dimmers. The development of a single-source instrument with a complete range of direct color control would reduce the size and number of instruments and number of control elements required.

C. FORM

The form of light distribution is presently dependent on a selection of fixed mounting positions and directions for the various types of instruments; thus, the range of form variation is limited. However, an effective change in form can be accomplished by varying the intensity of one or several instruments, thereby shifting the total form. Spotlights may be remotely controlled as to direction and spread of light, however, the control circuitry required complicates operation and is too expensive to justify general usage. At the present time, the most obvious sense of form is derived from the shape, position, texture, and painted detail of scenic elements.

D. MOVEMENT

Movement is the dynamic element of lighting. As any change in a physical object necessitates the concept of time, any change in light necessitates the concept of movement: any change in the physical dimensions of length, width, and depth occur in time, and any change in the light dimensions of intensity, color, and form occur in movement. If changes of intensity, color, and form are to be consistent with the desired dramatic effect, the changes must be controlled so as not to call attention to themselves as lighting "effects" or tricks. Dimming and the resulting changes must be either intricately cued if the control is decentralized, or must be under the centralized control of a chief operator.

II. ELECTRICAL CONSIDERATIONS

The electrical control of stage lighting affords the designer and the electrician with a tool which, when properly understood and applied, can achieve effects that greatly enhance a stage presentation. Anyone who hopes to use effectively electrical lighting control systems can understand their application, operation, and intent through a knowledge of the basic principles of electricity and electrical control.

Should the reader be required to deal with the more complex circuitry of electronic control systems, he should refer to electrical texts and handbooks for a broader and more definitive treatment of the physics of electricity.

A. BASIC ELECTRICITY

Electrical phenomena depend on negatively charged atomic particles, electrons, which have been dislodged from their orbital paths about the nucleus of an atom. These free electrons are usually moving at random in a conductor; they are forced into an orderly movement when a source of electromotive force is applied to the conductor. This orderly movement, electric current, is accomplished by the attraction of the electrons toward the positive side of the source (opposite polarities attract), and the repulsion of the electrons away from the negative side of the source (like polarities repel). The difference in the charges of the positive (deficiency of electrons) and the negative (excess of electrons) terminals of the source, is called the potential difference. (Potential is defined as the ability to do work). As the electrons move from the higher potential toward the lower potential, they jump from one atom to the next. This motion of electron drift is comparatively slow, however the combined effect, or electrical impulse travels through the conductor at the speed of light (186,264 miles per second).

As the electron current flows through the conductor, it is subjected to resistance, or opposition to current flow. Since current flow depends on the number of free electrons available in the material, conductors may be defined as materials with many free electrons, and insulators may be defined as materials with very few free electrons. The number of free electrons in a material determines its resistivity; the resistance of a material is directly proportional to the length and inversely proportional to the cross-sectional area.

Resistance = resistivity x $\dfrac{\text{length}}{\text{area}}$.

Electrical energy flowing through a resistance is dissapated as heat.

B. OHM'S LAW

The size of the current that can flow through a given resistance is determined by the applied electromotive force, emf, or electrical pressure. This relationship of resistance to quantatative current and applied electrical pressure is defined by Ohm's law: The current flowing in an electrical circuit is directly proportional to the applied electromotive force, and inversely proportional to the resistance of the circuit, when the current is stated in amperes, the electromotive force in volts, and the resistance in ohms. Power, or the rate of doing work, is electrically stated in terms of watts. Wattage is the product of voltage and amperage.

$I \text{ (amps)} = \dfrac{E \text{ (volts)}}{R \text{ (ohms)}}$; $P \text{ (watts)} = I \text{ (amps)} \times E \text{ (volts)}$. These relationships apply to direct current, or a current which flows along a conductor in one direction. Batteries are the most common electro-chemical source of direct current, DC; rectifiers provide direct current from standard alternating current power sources.

C. ELECTRO-MAGNETISM

A current flowing through a conductor produces a magnetic field at right angles to the axis of the conductor. If a straight insulated conductor is wound into a coil, the small magnetic fields around each segment of the conductor reinforce each other to create a concentrated magnetic field around the coil. Conversely, a magnetic field generates an electrical current in a conductor, when the conductor is moved through the field so that it cuts the lines of magnetic force. An electric generator utilizes this principle in changing mechanical energy into electrical energy.

D. CIRCUITS

An electrical circuit is defined as a closed loop providing an unbroken flow path from the negative terminal of the source, through the various conductors and components, and back to the positive terminal of the source. Circuits may contain one or more possible paths of current flow; an incomplete, broken, or open circuit is a circuit in which a component or conductor prevents the flow of current; a switch opens a circuit in the off position, and closes the circuit in the on position; a fuse or circuit breaker automatically opens the circuit if the current flow rate is too high, as might be caused by a short, in which the current does not flow through an effective resistance, but instead flows from the negative terminal to the positive terminal of the source.

1. Series Circuit

    A series circuit is a circuit in which the current flows consecutively through each component; there is only one possible path for current flow. In a series circuit, the current is the same in each component part. The voltage drop, or difference of potential, across a resistance varies in direct proportion to the resistance.

2. Parallel Circuit

    A parallel circuit is a circuit in which there are two or more possible paths for current flow. In the parallel circuit, the voltage drop across each component part is the same, and the current through each component varies indirectly with the resistance.

3. Series-Parallel Circuit

    A series parallel circuit is a circuit composed of both series and parallel elements. Such circuits should be analyzed by combining resistances in each portion of the circuit into equivalent single resistances, and the resulting simple circuit analyzed as a series or parallel circuit. In cases of more complex circuits, Kirchhoff's laws may be useful in circuit analysis: The sum of the currents flowing toward any one point in a circuit is equal to the sum of the currents flowing away from that point; the sum of the electromotive forces applied to any one loop of a circuit is equal to the sum of the voltage drops across each resistance in that loop.

E. ALTERNATING CURRENT

Electric generators produce either direct current (current flow is unidirectional) or alternating current (current flow reverses periodically). In its simplest form an AC generator consists of a loop of wire (the armature) rotating between the two poles of a magnet. The rotation of the loop through a complete circle (360°) is called one cycle, in which the current flows in one direction, reaches a peak value at 90°, decreases in value to zero at 180°, declines (rises in a reverse direction) to a negative peak at 270°, and returns to zero value at 360°.

1. Sine wave

    The plotting of this cycle results in the sine curve, with the horizontal base line representing time (measured in degrees of rotation of the loop) and the vertical axis representing amplitude (positive above the base line, and negative below the base line).

2. Frequency (f = frequency)

    The number of complete cycles occurring during a time period of one cycle is called the frequency.

3. Phase angle ($\emptyset$ = phase; Θ = angle)

    If two periodic quantities alternate at the same frequency, but start at different times, the time lapse between the start of the first and the start of the second is called the phase difference; when expressed in degrees, this difference is called the phase angle. The quantity which starts its cycle first is said to lead the other quantity, which lags the former.

F. INDUCTION

1. Self inductance

    Whenever magnetic flux lines cut across a conductor, an electrical current is induced in the conductor. If the conductor is wound into a coil, and connected to an alternating current source, the rise and fall of the alternating current value will create an expanding and decaying magnetic field, which induces a current in turns of the coil as it cuts across them. This counter or back electromotive force is equal to but flowing in the opposite direction from the original current, and opposing the flow of the original current. If power is not drawn from the counter emf current, very little current will flow through the coil. If, however, current is drawn from the "induced secondary", the current flow through the coil will be directly proportional to the current draw on the secondary. The auto-transformer utilizes this principle of self-inductance. The line leads are connected across the coil, and one of the load leads is connected to one end of the coil, common with one of the line leads. The other load lead is connected to a movable tap, which can be connected at any turn of the coil to provide a variable voltage to the load.

2. Mutual inductance

    Mutual inductance occurs when the magnetic field of one coil cuts across the turns of an adjacent coil. The primary coil connected to the alternating current source, induces a voltage in the secondary coil by means of the rising and falling magnetic field cutting across the adjacent turns of the secondary coil connected to the load.

    a. Transformers

        Coils coupled by mutual inductance are called transformers. To obtain the optimum linkage between the two coils, a closed iron core is frequently used to concentrate the magnetic lines of force. The ratio of primary to secondary voltages is approximately equal to the ratio of the number of turns of the primary coil to the number of turns of the secondary coil. The magnetizing force of a coil is stated as the product of the current flowing in the coil and the number of turns. Since the magnetizing forces must be nearly equal in both the primary and the secondary coils, it follows that the current varies inversely with the voltage, i.e., when the voltage is stepped up, the current is stepped down.

46

3. Current voltage relation in inductance: Current lags the voltage by 90°. Opposition of current flow is called <u>inductive reactance.</u>

G. CAPACITANCE

Capacitance is the ratio of the charge of two conductors, separated by a dielectric or insulating material, to the potential difference between the conductors. A capacitor is a device which, when connected to a DC source will collect an electrical charge of a potential equal to that of the applied emf. When an AC voltage is applied to a capacitor, the plates alternately charge and discharge, allowing the current to effectively flow "through" the capacitor. The current in a capacitive circuit leads the voltage by 90°.

1. Capacitive reactance

A capacitor imposes an opposition to current flow, which is called capacitive reactance. This reactance is inversely proportional to the capacitance and the frequency by a factor of 2π, when the frequency is expressed in cycles per second, the capacitance in farads, and the capacitive reactance in ohms.

H. IMPEDANCE

Impedance is the total opposition to the flow of alternating current imposed in a circuit containing resistance inductive reactance, and capacitive reactance.

1. Reactance

Due to the 90° lead of voltage in pure inductance, and the 90° lag of voltage in pure capacitance, the inductive reactance may be considered positive, and the capacitive reactance considered negative; the two reactances may thus be added algebraically.

2. Impedance

Since reactance does not dissipate electrical energy, but temporarily stores it in magnetic or electric fields, it may not be arithmetically added to resistance. In order to determine the net effect of resistance and reactance in the same circuit, the two quantities may be added vectorially, the impedance being represented by the hypotenuse of a right triangle, the resistance represented by the horizontal leg, and the net reactance represented by the vertical leg; the included angle between the hypotenuse and the resistance leg represents the phase angle. This relationship may be stated trigonometrically:

$$\tan (\text{phase angle}) = \frac{\text{reactance}}{\text{resistance}} .$$

3. Ohm's law for AC circuits

Ohm's law may be applied to alternating current circuits by substituting impedance for resistance: $\text{Current} = \dfrac{\text{electromotive force}}{\text{reactance}}$

I. COMMERCIAL DISTRIBUTION OF ELECTRIC POWER

The standard electric power commercially distributed in the United States is alternating current at 60 cycles per second. The <u>two wire system</u> is used for branch circuits; one wire is "hot", and the other is "neutral". Each wire is connected to one side of the load. In new installations, the electrical code requires the use of a third <u>"ground" wire;</u> this grounding wire does not normally carry a current, and is attached to all metal electrical enclosures, such as equipment cabinets, instrument hoods, switchboard frames, conduit, outlet boxes, etc. In case one of the current carrying wires comes into contact with electrical enclosures, this grounding wire provides a path for current flow, thereby preventing a person who contacts such a shorted enclosure from being shocked. <u>The three wire, single phase system</u> has three "legs", with the voltage in each leg 120° out of phase with the other legs. <u>In the Wye-connected</u>

47

configuration, the current in any line is the same as the current in any winding, but the voltage across any two lines is 1.73 times the voltage across any one winding. In the delta-connected configuration, the voltage across any two lines is equal to the voltage across any individual winding, and the current is 1.73 times the current in any winding. Three hot wires and one neutral are used in the Wye configuration; the neutral wire is not used in the delta connection.

J. ELECTRONICS

Electronic devices are used to control a relatively large electrical quantity by means of a small control quantity.

1. Tube

In the electron tube, a cathode emits electrons when heated to incandescence; these electrons are attracted to the anode (positive element of the tube). By imposing a control element (grid) between the cathode and anode, the relatively large plate current may be effectively controlled by electrically deflecting the electron current away from the anode by means of a potential applied on the control element.

2. Semi-conductors

In semi-conductor devices, the effective flow of current is possible in only one direction: from the negatively biased element to the positively biased element. If a control element is imposed between the two, a relatively high voltage current may be controlled by varying the current in the control element.

3. Electronic Control Devices

Heavy current devices, such as the thyratron tube and the silicon controlled rectifier, are essentially high speed switching devices; i.e., they will shift from a non-conducting state to a conducting state when the value applied to their control element reaches a certain point, i.e., the device will turn on or "fire". When an AC load current is to be controlled, effective scalar control can be achieved by firing the device after the sine wave has crossed the zero base line; by varying the point at which the device fires, the effective, or average, voltage delivered to the load may be varied. Essentially, the phase of the control value is made to lag the phase of the load value. Conduction ceases when the load value crosses the zero base line, and the device remains in a non-conducting state for the next half cycle plus the load-control lag time. By use of two such devices, connected in a back to back arrangement, the load current can be controlled on each half cycle—one device controls the positive half cycles, and the other device controls the negative half cycles.

K. CODE

The National Electrical Code (Standards of the National Board of Fire Underwriters for Electric Wiring and Devices), as recommended by the National Fire Protection Association, is generally accepted throughout the United States for determining the safe and legal construction and use of electrical wiring and devices. In most instances local codes correspond with the national code; however, in case of variations between the local code and the national code, the local code governs. Article 520 of the national code deals specifically with "Theatres and Assembly Halls". The code is published in book form, and is available from most booksellers and electrical equipment distributors. Standard commercially manufactured equipment is constructed to comply with code specifications; any special or custom devices should be constructed to comply with code regulations so as to provide safe load carrying capacities, sufficient electrical and heat insulation, and to provide safe and reliable operation.

III. PARTS AND TERMINOLOGY

Frequently used electrical terminologies are listed and defined for reference usage.

- A -

<u>Alignment.</u> Arrangement of components or parts in either vertical or horizontal rows.

<u>Alternating Current (AC).</u> A flow of electrons in which the electrons periodically reverse their direction of flow.

<u>Alternator.</u> A generator of alternating current.

<u>Ampere (amp).</u> The unit of electrical current.

<u>Amplifier.</u> A group of components so connected as to achieve the control of a small current value.

<u>Anode.</u> The positive element of an electron tube, semi-conductor device, battery, etc.

<u>Auto-transformer.</u> A transformer which uses the principle of self-induction. One coil is used as both the primary and the secondary of the transformer.

- B -

<u>Bank.</u> (1) A horizontal row of dimmers or other components.
(2) A rack or cabinet containing amplifier dimmers, contactors, etc.

<u>Bias.</u> A DC value applied to an electronic element so as to maintain the applied AC value at a desired relationship to the zero base line.

<u>Board.</u> (generally "switchboard") The general term applied to a grouping of control elements into a cabinet or rack mounted assembly.

<u>Bus.</u> A copper bar or wire used as a common electrical connection, or as a conductor for high currents.

- C -

<u>Cable.</u> (1) A wire used as an electrical conductor. (2) A group of separately insulated electrical conductors (usually two or three) enclosed in a common fabric or rubber sheath, with male and female connectors on opposite ends; used for extension of electrical service from permanent wiring to a portable load such as a lighting instrument.

<u>Capacitor.</u> An electrical device for storing electrical charges; consists of two conductors (usually plates) separated by a dielectric.

<u>Capacity.</u> (1) A wattage or amperage rating of the current that can be safely and efficiently carried by an electrical device. (2) The size of an electrical charge that can be stored in a capacitor.

<u>Cathode.</u> The negative element of an electron tube, semi-conductor, etc.

<u>Choke.</u> An inductive device which imposes opposition to the flow of an alternating current, or opposes a change in the flow of a current.

<u>Circuit.</u> An arrangement of conductors and other electrical elements so as to permit a flow of electrons from one terminal of a source, through the various conductors and circuit elements, and back to the other terminal of the source.

<u>Circuit breaker.</u> A protective device which switches a circuit to off when the current value exceeds

a predetermined limit. Current sensing element may be thermal or electromagnetic.

Company switch. A large capacity service switch usually located at the side of the proscenium; contains terminals and fuses for the connection of portable control boards to the electrical service.

Conductor. A substance, usually metal, which has a low resistivity, thus permits current flow with a minimum of resistance.

Connector. A two part (male and female) device for making temporary electrical and mechanical circuit connections.

Console. A compact grouping of control elements, usually placed so the operator can see the stage.

Contactor. A switch actuated by a remotely controlled solenoid (electromagnet). The solenoid is operated by a small current, which can control a large current at the switch.

Controller. A manually controlled device for establishing a desired relationship in an electrical circuit. The controller usually controls a pilot current or voltage, which is used to operate the load carrying device, such as a contactor or amplifier dimmer.

Cross-connecting panel. A panel at which the load or stage circuits terminate in male connectors, and the control or dimmer circuits terminate in female connectors. By means of jumpers or cables similar to telephone switchboard cables, the load circuit may be connected to any dimmer circuit. Usually several jacks (female connectors) are provided for each dimmer circuit, so that more than one load circuit may be placed on each dimmer circuit.

Cross-metering. A form of cross-connecting which uses a vertical grid imposed over, but not contacting a horizontal grid. Each of the grids is composed of bus bars, with one load or dimmer circuit connected to each of the bars (all dimmer circuits on one grid, and all load circuits on the other grid). By using sliding connectors, a horizontal bar may be connected to a vertical bar at an appropriate juncture, thus permitting any load circuit to be connected to any dimmer circuit.

Current (I). The drift or flow of electrons through a conductor. The size or volume of current flow is measured in amperes.

Cycle. One complete revolution of an AC generator, in which the current and voltage rises from zero value, increases to a maximum falls to zero, rises to a maximum value in the opposite direction, and again returns to zero value.

- D -

Dead-front or dead-face. All electrically live parts are covered by either insulating panels, or metal panels connected to ground potential.

Dielectric. An insulating material.

Dimmer. A device for controlling the current or voltage available to a lamp, thereby controlling the intensity of the lamp load connected to the dimmer.

Diode. A two element electronic tube containing a cathode or anode, or a two pole semiconductor device which allows current to flow in only one direction (A rectifier or detector).

Direct current (DC). A flow of electrons in one direction; after the initial rise from zero value (turn-on) the current and voltage values do not cross the zero value base line, and current flow does not reverse.

50

Electromagnet. A magnet composed of a soft iron core and a coil of insulated wire wound around the core. An electric current passing through the coil generates a magnetic field which is concentrated in the soft iron core.

Electromotive force (emf or E). The force which produces an electric current in a circuit.

Extended or foreign control. A remote pushbutton switch used to control a sectional master, grand master, or house light contactor.

Fader. A device (variable resistance potentiometer or auto-transformer) for gradually transferring from one set of dimmer readings to another set.

Farad. The unit of capacitance. Usually expressed in micro—or micro-micro farads (mfd or mmfd)

Filament. The resistive heater element in a tube, or the resistive light-producing element in an incandescent lamp.

Filter. A configuration of resistive, inductive, and capacitive devices, used to reduce or oppose undesired current and voltage characteristics.

Frequency. The number of cycles occuring during a time period of one second. Usually cycles per second (cps).

Fuse. A current limiting device, consisting of an alloy conductor which melts, thereby opening the circuit when current flow exceeds the rated capacity. Types: (1) Plug. Fuse element is mounted in a screw base. (2) Cartridge. Fuse element is mounted in a cylinder of fiber composition the ends of which are capped with metal to permit connection of the fuse element into the circuit. (3) Knife blade. A cartridge type with blade end contacts, rather than caps. In addition to current carrying ability, fuses are rated as to operating time, i. e., the time required for the fuse element to open when subjected to a specified load. Extremely fast acting fuses are required to protect semi-conductor devices from high overcurrents, while slow operating fuses are required in motor circuits, to prevent the circuit from opening while the motor is starting and drawing a high current.

Gain. The amplification ratio (1:x) of control value to load value in a control device, such as an electron tube.

Generator. A device for changing mechanical, chemical, or light energy into electrical energy.

Grand master. The master switch or contactor which controls all stage lighting circuits.

Grid. An open network consisting of vertical and horizontal lines, such as a screen. (1) The control element of an electron tube. (2) The open steel structure over the stage house, from which stage scenery, lights, etc. are suspended.

Ground. Zero potential; connected to earth.

Group. A number of dimmers under the control of one dimmer or switch.

House board. A permanently connected or fixed switchboard serving as permanent equipment of a theatre building. Professionally used to control only house lights, and, infrequently, foot lights and border lights.

Ignitron. A heavy duty electronic tube utilizing a mercury pool cathode. A pointed electrode (ignitor) is used to trigger the mercury vapor discharge and start conduction within the tube.

Independent. An individual circuit not controlled by a group, scene, or preset master control.

Inductor. A device which produces a voltage by means of the relative motion of a magnetic field across a conductor.

Inter-connecting. The ability to connect any load to any control by means of a cross-connecting apparatus (See Cross-connecting).

Interlocking. (1) A mechanical means for operating two or more control elements by means of a single master lever or wheel. (2) An electrical or electronic control circuit or mechanical device designed to prevent the operation of circuit or device until another circuit or device has been positioned or operated correctly. For example, the door of a master disconnect switch is interlocked so that it may not be opened until the switch has been thrown to the off position, and the switch may not be turned on until the door is closed.

Inter-plugging. Cross-connecting system using plugs and jacks.

- J -

Jack. The female element of an electrical connector, usually of the telephone type.

Jumper. A cable equipped with suitable connectors used for the temporary connection of two components or circuits, as in the cross-connecting panel.

- L -

Lead. A single electrical conductor or cable.

Line. The feed or source side of a wiring layout. Often called "live" or "hot".

Load. (1) The total power consumption in a circuit, usually rated in watts.
(2) The total current requirements of a circuit, usually rated in amperes.
(3) The side of a wiring layout containing power consuming devices.

- M -

Magnetic Amplifier. A dimming device using a reactance coil connected in series with a blocking rectifier, so that conduction occurs only on alternate half cycles of the alternating load current. Control is accomplished by a DC current flowing through a control winding, which saturates or de-saturates the magnetic core on which the coils are wound, thereby decreasing or increasing the opposition to AC current flow in the load coil. When the coil is fully saturated, the opposition is minimum and the maximum load current flows. The blocking rectifier makes the load current independent of the control current (a higher load value does not require a higher control value) and permits a much faster response time than possible with the older reactance dimmer circuit.

Marker. An identification tag, containing a letter, number, or name mounted on or near a control element or conductor.

Marking dial. A calibrated scale used to indicate the setting of a dimmer controller or handle. Usually graduated in 10 points, with quarter point markings, reading from 0 (off) to 10 (full on).

Master control. A switch or dimmer used to control a grouping of individual switches or dimmers.

Meter. A device for measuring electrical characteristics of a circuit, such as voltage, amperage, wattage.

- N -

Neutral. The zero potential conductor. Never fused in AC circuits.

- O -

Ohm (Ω). The unit of electrical resistance (R).

Open circuit. A circuit in which a break in an electrical component prevents the flow of current.

Operating light. A low intensity lamp used to illuminate working surfaces of a control board or console.

Operator. The person who runs the control board during a performance.

Outlet. The service or feed end of a connection.

Overload. A load greater than that which circuit components can safely and efficiently carry.

- P -

Parallel. A circuit configuration in which current may flow in two or more paths, at the same time.

Parallel blade connector. A connector utilizing two flat blades of a conducting metal, in a parallel relationship. The standard household electrical connector.

Patch panel. A cross-connecting panel.

Phase ($\emptyset$). Electrical time, as stated in terms of degrees of rotation of an AC generator, or, a wave which starts at a certain electrical time in relation to waves starting at other times.

Piano box. A portable switchboard enclosed in an upright castered wooden box, containing resistance dimmers, switches, plugs, fuses, and work lights.

Pilot light. An indicator light used to indicate operational conditions of a control circuit.

Pin connector. A connector utilizing one or more cylindrical or rod shaped pins of a conducting metal. Usually two or three pins mounted in a fibre block, or molded into a rubber sheath.

Plug. The male element of a connector.

Plugging box. A portable box containing one electrical feed to two or more branch circuits terminating in female connectors. Sometimes contains branch fuses.

Pocket. A permanently installed box containing female connectors for servicing one or more stage circuits. Usually installed at frequently used positions about the stage floor, at the tormentors, on light pipes, in the grid, etc.

Potential. The amount of electrical charge held by a body, in comparison with another point or body. Measured in volts.

Preset. (1) To set intensity levels for a scene. (2) A bank of alternate controls which may be energized by means of a preset switch or fader. The preset control configuration allows one bank of preset controls to be set for a following scene, while another bank of preset controls is energized.

Primary: The line or source side of an electrical circuit, usually a transformer.

Reactance.   The opposition to the flow of an electric current by inductance, capacitance, or both.

Reactor.   A device which opposes the flow of an alternating current by means of inductance, capac-itance, or both.

Reactor dimmer.   An early form of the magnetic amplifier dimmer using an inductance coil in the load circuit.   The load coil and the control coil are wound on an eight-shaped saturable core of magnetic material.   By varying the DC current in the (center) control coil, the core satu-rates or desaturates, thereby controlling the flow of current in the load coil.   The control cur-rent is related to the load current, i.e., a larger load requires a larger control value, and the response time is relatively slow.

Reading.   A dimmer or dimmer controller setting.

Rectifier.   A device which permits current flow through it in only one direction; used to change alternating current into direct current.

Relay.   An electro-magnetic switching device, used as a remote or automatic control.   A relay is similar to a contactor, however, in general usage, a relay controls small currents, and a contactor controls large currents.

Remote control.   Control of a circuit from a remote location, by means of low current operated devices, which control higher currents; relays, contactors, dimmer amplifiers, etc.

Resistance.   (R) The simple mechanical opposition to current flow.   Measured in ohms.

Resistor.   A device which imposes resistance to the flow of an electrical current.

Response time.   The time required for a device to function; the time lag between the operation of a control and the effect of the operation.

Rheostat.   A variable resistor.

Root-mean-square.   The effective value of an AC voltage or current, producing the same heating effect as a DC value of equivalent size.   The RMS value of 60 cycle alternating current is .707 times the maximum value.

Secondary.   The load side of an electrical circuit, usually a transformer.

Section.   A group of related components, usually in the same row.

Semi-conductor.   A solid state electronic device constructed of materials which function as either insulators or conductors, depending on current values and polarities applied to them.

Series.   A circuit configuration in which current may flow in only one path, successively through each of the circuit components.

Setting.   The scalar position of a control device, such as a dimmer handle.

Setup.   (1) The process of preparing the stage scenery and lighting for a technical rehearsal.
(2) The process of setting preset controls for a following scene. (3) a preset.

Shaft.   A rod to which individual resistance or auto-transformer dimmer control handles may be interlocked for non-proportional master control.

Shoe.   A movable sliding contact surface.

Short circuit. A circuit in which no effective load is imposed, and the current may flow from one source terminal to the other without passing through current limiting components.

Solenoid. An electromagnetic coil which is used to operate a movable magnetic plunger. When the coil, usually wound around a hollow tube, is energized, the magnetic field draws the plunger into the coil.

Step. An increment, usually between the contacts of a resistance or auto-transformer dimmer.

Sub-master control. An intermediate switch or dimmer between the individual controls and the master controls. A sub-master controls a group of individual controls and a master controls a group of sub-masters.

Surge. A high current flow or voltage which occurs during transition states, such as during the switching on of a circuit.

Switch. A device for the on or off control of a current.

- T -

Thyratron. An electronic switching tube with a cathode, anode, and control grid. The tube turns on or fires when the value applied to the control grid reaches the characteristic value for turn on. Once the tube has fired, the control element can not turn the device off; the external load must be turned off before the grid can regain control.

Timer. A device for energizing a circuit after a predetermined time delay, or a device for accomplishing a control operation within a predetermined period of time.

Transformer. A device composed of two or more coils, linked by magnetic lines of force, and used to transfer energy from one electrical circuit to another. The ratio of the input voltage to the output voltage is approximately equal to the ratio of the number of turns in the primary to the number of turns in the secondary.

Transducer. A device for converting energy from one form or system to another, i. e. , changing mechanical energy into electrical energy.

Transistor. An electronic control device composed of two or more semi-conductor elements.

Tube. An electronic device enclosed within an evacuated or inert gas filled enclosure, and used for switching, rectification, amplification, etc. in electronic circuits.

Twist-Lock (trade name) connector. A connector utilizing arc shaped blades which mechanically lock when the male connector is twisted into the female connector, thus providing an electrical connection which can not be broken by mechanical tension on the cables.

- V -

Volt (V). The unit of electrical potential.

- W -

Watt (W). The unit of electrical power.

Winding. A coil of an insulated conductor, in an inductive device, such as a transformer, electro-magnet, or solenoid.

IV. DIMMERS AND CONTROL SYSTEMS

Early attempts to control lighting intensity and color for dramatic effects included raising and lowering fixtures behind baffles or bottles of colored water or wine, snuffing the lamps by hand, lighting them by spirit soaked wicks, and turning colored cylinders across the face of the oil lamp. These systems were not overly effective, since they involved the placing of an operator at each lamp, or a complicated arrangement of strings, wires, pulleys, levers, and rods to perform mechanically such operations from a central point. Gas lighting eventually replaced the oil lamp and candle and their associated problems of control (one of which was perhaps preventing the lighting technician from drinking the color media?). Since gas lighting required a supply line, the gas table was installed and used to control the distribution of the incoming supply to the various lights about the stage. This gas table consisted of a series of master, sub-master, and individual valves, which, by limiting the flow rate, could dim smoothly the gas lights. In fact, the flexibility and smoothness of control possible with the gas table far excelled the subsequent resistance dimmer control; it is only with the advent of electronic dimming control that we have begun to approach the flexibility and smoothness of control afforded by the early gas tables.

Eventually the economic and safety advantages of electricity as a power source for stage lighting forced gas lighting and the gas control table out of existence. Several control methods were attempted as a replacement for the gas table: the salt-water dimmer, the carbon pile dimmer, and the resistance dimmer. The resistance dimmer survived, although it only partially solved the problems of electrical control of intensity. At the time a dimming device which consumed electrical energy and prevented delivery of the consumed energy to the lamp was most feasible. To achieve mastering and sub-mastering of such power consuming devices, each control element had to be capable of handling and dissipating power in the form of heat. Thus a system using electrical mastering required a large number of such power handling devices, and was consequently complicated, expensive, and hot. Another mastering approach was to use a mechanical system for linking and interlocking individual controls to a master control; this mechanical mastering system required extensive shafts, cams, and gears reminiscent of factories at the turn of the century. Although industrial technology soon replaced the intricate shafting and gearing with individual power sources and controls, theatre technology (apparently figuring refinement of such complicated mechanisms as an improper insult to the spirit of theatrical mystery) kept what they had—namely problems of mechanical alignment and a system which did not provide the proportional dimming control necessary for sublet lighting, nor the compactness of control elements required if the lighting operator was to be stationed in a position where he could see the lighting effects on the stage. Due to the friction inherent in such mechanical linkages, operation of several interlocked dimmers required an overweight electrician to provide the mechanical push necessary to move a group of interlocked dimmers.

The first electric control boards used exposed wiring and switches. The safety hazards presented by such exposed electrical components finally resulted in the specification of the dead-face type of board (in which all electrical components are mounted behind insulating or electrically grounded panels) by the National Electrical Code. In the early forms of control boards, the switches were so large that the dimmers had to be racked above the switch banks in an inconvenient and unrelated position. Eventually the hazards and operating problems relegated these control boards to a balcony at the side of the stage, thereby decreasing operator visibility and usefulness. As lighting aesthetics developed, house boards proved inadequate to handle the lighting of a production, so it became customary for traveling professional companies to carry their own portable switch boards, specially designed for each production. Thus, the house boards were left with the control of only house lights and secondary stage lighting loads.

The rise of the presentation house and the repertory opera stage lent new impetus to the requirements for a house board capable of efficiently controlling all stage lighting instruments. These requirements for such a control system eventually culminated in such control boards as those at the Radio City Music Hall, and the old Metropolitan Opera House. Although not ideal, such systems using electronic and reactor control elements were far superior to the resistance boards.

Eventually, the requirements of educational and non-commerical repertory theatres led to the development of the fully electronic remote control system. The prototype installation, using thyratron tube dimmer amplifiers was installed at the Yale University Theatre in 1947. Since the introduction of this system by George C. Izenour, the application of semi-conductor devices to the control principles set forth in the design of this system, has advanced the art of stage lighting more in the past ten years than in the previous fifty years. Systems utilizing solid state circuitry are far more dependable than earlier systems, and are quite compatible with the aesthetic requirements for sensitive control and centralized operation.

The aim of remote control is two-fold: first, to afford the lighting designer with a position from which he can, during lighting rehearsals, observe and control the stage lighting picture, and secondly, to relieve the control operator of routine tasks. Once the designer has achieved the lighting picture he desires, it is simply a matter of recording the settings of the various controllers and turning these over to the control operator for use during performance. By the addition of preset boards, the operator can set the various dimmer readings before the scene, or before the performance, providing sufficient presets are provided. The development of the punched data card preset system by George Izenour and David Locklin eliminated the task of writing preset cue sheets and setting the readings on the preset boards. In such an automated data system, the system memorizes the dimmer reading; the operator can concentrate on subtleties of timing, fading, and synchronization, rather than being concerned with the routine and mistake-laden setting of dimmer readings either on cue or in preset banks.

With the older control systems in which the operator was hidden from the stage and had little concept of the lighting picture, the lighting designer had to cue, coax, and curse to achieve the lighting he wanted; once achieved in a lighting rehearsal, it was rarely ever that it was reduplicated during performance. Such a process is not contributary to good tempers or good lighting.

By the use of low current, low voltage control circuitry, the control functions of individual, master, and sub-master dimming need not be accomplished in power handling stages; only after such controlling is accomplished is the control signal fed to the actual dimming device. Thus, the size of control elements can be compact and arranged for maximum ease of operation; with the automation of presetting, and the reduction of controller space requirements, one operator can handle all the control functions for a production, and can be located at a position where he can see the stage picture. Thus, the art of stage lighting control has advanced to the point where flexible and sensitive control, compatible with the concepts of the lighting designer, can be achieved. This is not to say that the ideal control system has evolved; it hasn't. However, the manufacturers of lighting equipment are cognizant of advances in other fields of technology, and are investigating the application of these advances to lighting control. Too, the renewed interest in the community repertory theatre and the educational theatre has shifted the emphasis from the commercial theatre and its limited production capabilities to a more experimental and artistic theatre of community culture. Performing arts centers are being proposed and built in many areas of the country; each has its own personality and production concept, and each requires different equipment to explore these philosophies of the performing arts. Thus, the age of stereotyped theatres, and consequent stereotyped lighting control systems is over: the lighting equipment manufacturers have to think in terms of flexibility, and how modern technology can provide flexibility.

A. DIMMERS

The dimmer is a means of reducing the current or voltage of a circuit, thereby reducing the light output from a lamp load connected to the dimmer.

1. The resistance dimmer

The resistance dimmer consists essentially of a long resistance wire and a sliding shoe used to vary the length of the resistance wire in the circuit. The dimmer is connected in series with the lamp load to be controlled.

a. In an electrical circuit, the current flow is proportional to the applied electromotive force, and inversely proportional to the resistance ($I = \frac{E}{R}$); thus, by increasing the resistance of a circuit, the power delivered to a lamp is decreased thereby accomplishing a dimming effect.

b. The wire in a resistance dimmer must be sufficiently long to provide smooth dimming of the lamp. In order to achieve this dimming, the resistance of the dimmer element has to be approximately five times the resistance of the lamp load. The resistance wire is usually coiled to reduce its physical length, embedded in a vitreous cement to provide mechanical protection, and tapped at convenient intervals to give a series of steps with segments of the resistance wire between each step. A shoe connected to the dimmer handle rides over these steps, thereby varying the effective resistance of the dimmer. Since the eye is not sensitive to large changes of intensity when the general brightness is high, the taps connected to the resistance wire are spaced at larger intervals at the top end (high intensity) than the low end (low intensity).

c. The resistance dimmer is available in two basic forms: the slide dimmer and the plate dimmer.

(1) The slide dimmer is available in lower wattage ratings, and has few steps, thus is useful primarily for setting intensity levels which do not require change in view of the audience. It can not be interlocked.

(2) The plate dimmer, in general usage, has a resistance element cemented to a metal or soap stone base of a round or rectangular shape, with the resistance wire arranged in a star form, and the taps arranged in a circular form. It is available in capacities up to 3600 watts in the 18" diameter plate, and up to 6000 watts in the rectangular form.

d. The size of the dimmer is directly proportional to the amount of power to be dissipated.

e. Disadvantages of the resistance dimmer are:

(1) It dissipates electrical energy in the form of heat, and is thus wasteful (unless it is used to heat cold backstage areas).

(2) Since the ratio of approximately five to one dimmer resistance to lamp load must be maintained for smooth dimming, the dimmer is effective only at its rated load capacity.

(3) The dimmer is bulky, heavy, hot, and requires direct manual or mechanically interlocked operation.

2. The auto-transformer dimmer

The auto-transformer dimmer consists of an induction coil serving as both primary and secondary transformer circuits, operating on the principle of self-induction.

a. Each end of the coil is connected to the line leads; the sliding contact shoe and one end of the coil are connected to the load leads. The sliding shoe operates across taps from the induction coil.

b. The alternating current flowing through the full length of the coil produces a magnetic flux which, in turn, induces a back-emf in the same coil. By tapping the coil with a sliding shoe, a variable voltage is available which is directly proportional to the number of turns between the load leads. This voltage is independent of the power drawn by the secondary, thus the auto-transformer draws only the power required to operate the load, and the voltage across the secondary is independent of the secondary load. In other words, the dimmer can operate any load up to its full capacity, and no matter what the load is, the dimmer will always produce the same intensity at any one setting, independent of whether the connected load is large or small.

(1) If the sliding shoe touched only one tap at a time, there would be a flickering and arcing as the shoe moved off one contact and then on to the next; therefore, the shoe must touch a second contact before it leaves the preceeding one. This would

create a short circuit between contacts, resulting in a fairly high current flow. To overcome these two difficulties, the shoe is often made of carbon, which has sufficient resistance to prevent shorting of the turns of the coil, and is sufficiently large to contact two taps, thus preventing flickering and arcing.

c. Advantages of the auto-transformer dimmer are:

   (1)   It can control a variable load up to its maximum rating.

   (2)   It draws only the power required to operate the load, and does not dissipate power.

d. Disadvantages of the auto-transformer dimmer are:

   (1)   Auto-transformers are usually built to a straight line dimming curve, rather than the inverse square (logarithmic) eye sensitivity curve.

   (2)   Electrical mastering requires a power handling auto-transformer feeding the individual dimmers. Problems of mechanical mastering are the same as with the resistance dimmer.

   (3)   The auto-transformer is heavy and bulky; remote control (although it has been attempted with motorized control circuits) is unsatisfactory.

   (4)   Although not a serious disadvantage, the auto-transformer dimmer will operate only from AC.

   (5)   Requires relatively frequent maintenance.

3. The reactor dimmer

The reactor dimmer consists of a load carrying inductance coil and a control coil wound on a saturable magnetic core.

a. By applying a DC control current on the control coil, the core is made to saturate, thus allowing load current to flow through the load coil.

b. As the control current is reduced, the core desaturates, thus providing a reduction of the load current and a dimming effect.

c. The reactor construction varies; usually two load coils are used, and one control coil. The reactor dimmer can be used, with appropriate windings, to operate from either single phase or three phase primary. Thus the reactor can provide control of a large load by drawing a balanced current from each of three phases.

d. Advantages of the reactor dimmer are:

   (1)   It can be used to control large loads, and can automatically distribute the power drawn over three phases.

   (2)   The control element (a rheostat, usually rated at approximately 100 watts) or the tube rectifier can be remotely located from the power handling reactor.

e. Disadvantages of the reactor dimmer are:

   (1)   The control current is related to the load current, i.e., a large load requires more control current than a small load, thus the reactor, like the resistance dimmer, can operate effectively when loaded within a narrow margin of its rated load.

       (2)   The size of the windings and the core result in a large, heavy unit.

       (3)   Lag time (response) is slow.

   f.   Although the reactor dimmer has been largely replaced by the magnetic amplifier, it can be used to control large loads where response time is not critical, i. e., house lighting loads in large auditoriums.

4.   The magnetic amplifier dimmer

The magnetic amplifier dimmer is similar to the reactor dimmer, however, by the addition of a blocking diode, or rectifier, in the load circuit, quite different characteristics are obtained.

   a.   The rectifier is placed in series with the load coil.

   b.   Due to the action of the rectifier, current can flow through the coil on alternate half cycles (positive halves or negative halves, depending on the orientation of the diode).

   c.   The response time is much more rapid than that of the reactor dimmer.

   d.   The control current is independent of the load current.

   e.   Advantages of the magnetic amplifier dimmer are:

       (1)   Since the load current and the control current are independent, the dimmer can control any load up to its rated capacity.

       (2)   Response time is relatively fast.

       (3)   Coil and core sizes are smaller than those of the reactor dimmer.

       (4)   Few expendable parts such as tubes.

       (5)   Since control power requirements are small, the dimmer can be remotely controlled by a small pilot signal.

   f.   Disadvantages are:

       (1)   Weight, although not as great as that of the reactor dimmer, is still high.

       (2)   Response time not as small as that of the solid-state dimmer.

   g.   The magnetic amplifier, although it presently does not match the performance of solid-state electronic dimmers, is not inherently inferior. Due to the recent advances in solid-state physics and engineering, it seems that development of such dimming circuits (S C R) will be more rapid than in the magnetic amplifier field.

5.   The tube dimmer

The tube dimmer operates as a high-speed electronic switch, utilizing a thyratron power handling tube.

   a.   A phase shifted control signal is developed from the 60 cycle line frequency. This phase shift is accomplished by means of a variable resistor in a resistance-capacitance, or resistance-inductance circuit. Depending on the setting of the variable resistance, the control signal crosses the base line at a phase angle removed from the point where the line signal crosses the base line. By applying this phase shifted signal to the control grid of the thyratron, the tube can be made to conduct or fire after the line signal has crossed the zero base line, thus allowing only a portion of the sine wave to be delivered to the load. This delayed turn-on reduces the effective voltage delivered to the load, and thus creates a dimming effect. Since the tube will conduct in only one direction, it turns off when the line current crosses the zero base line, and reverses direction. This turns the tube off and allows the control grid to regain control.

b. Essentially, the dimmer operates as a switch turning the lamp on and off at a high speed synchronized with the line frequency. Due to the filament lag of the incandescent lamp, the light is not on sufficiently long to develop full intensity. The light output is proportional to the time the lamp is turned on during each cycle.

c. By using two tubes, one for each half of the sine wave cycle, the dimmer utilizes both halves of the cycle.

d. Advantages of the tube dimmer are:

   (1) Since only a very small low voltage current is required to control the dimmer, the control functions can be performed with small controllers, allowing a size compatible with remote control requirements.

   (2) The dimmer draws only the power required by the load.

   (3) Response time is fast.

   (4) Dimmers are multi-capacity: they can control any load up to their maximum rating.

e. Disadvantages of the tube dimmer:

   (1) Require relatively frequent service; since the tubes use a filament heater for the cathode, depending on usage, burn-out can be relatively frequent.

   (2) Due to the inherent tube resistance, there is a voltage drop in the tube. This frequently requires booster transformers if the dimmer is to deliver full voltage at a full intensity setting.

   (3) Tubes require warm-up before being subjected to power, thus the system must be turned on several minutes before dimming loads are placed on the tubes. The limited life and capacity of tube limits future prospects.

6. Solid state dimmers

Solid state dimmers make use of semi-conductor devices (silicon controlled rectifiers, SCR's) operating as high speed switches.

a. Generally, operation is similar to that of the tube circuit. The SCR is controlled by a phase shifted signal, which turns the device on for a portion of alternate half-cycles. The signal is applied to the "gate" of the SCR, which loses control once the device has fired, or shifted to a high conduction state. The device will conduct in only one direction, thus the conduction ceases and the gate regains control. The current flow crosses the zero base line and reverses.

b. Usually two rectifiers are used, one for each half of the cycle.

c. Advantages of the SCR dimmer:

   (1) Can be remotely controlled with devices of small size.

   (2) Dimmer draws only the power required by the load

61

(3)   Multi-capacity: can operate any load up to its maximum rating.

(4)   Response time is fast.

(5)   Voltage drop across the SCR is low; usually 2 to 4 volts, thus booster transformers are not required in a well designed circuit.

(6)   Dimmers require no warm-up period.

(7)   Size is small, weight is low.

d.   Disadvantages:

(1)   SCR's require protection (usually provided internal to the dimmer circuit) from high over-currents, and high ambient temperatures.

(2)   Output requires some filtering (usually internal to reduce the fast turn-on wave front, which causes hum or rattle in some lamp filaments.

e.   At the present time, the solid-state dimmer offers more in terms of control ability and cost than any other type of dimmer on the market. Since solid-state engineering is advancing rapidly, and more and more solid-state devices are being used in large industries, the cost of such devices is dropping, whereas most other costs are rising. Although the SCR device is the most used in the power handling stage of the dimmer, similar power handling devices are being developed, and might be applied to lighting control.

B.   CONTROL SYSTEMS

A control system consists of the dimmer, its control elements, and provisions for connecting the dimmer to the lighting loads.

1.   The portable switchboard (professional piano-box). The portable professional board is connected to service at the company switch and serves as a distribution point for the stage lighting loads.

a.   Resistance or auto-transformer dimmers (the latter are infrequent) are mounted on an angle iron frame at the bottom of the board. Dimmer spacing is uaually 4" from center to center.

(1)   Resistance: interlocking single or double plates from 250 watts to 3600 watts (dual capacity). Rectangular plates 5000 and 6000 watts.

(a)   6 or 12 500 or 750 watt plates mounted in smaller box, usually stacked on top of the piano box, serve as a preset board.

(b)   Piano box usually contains 14 1500/3000 watt dimmers, or 12 5000 watt dimmers.

(2)   Auto-transformer dimmers: 500 watt, 1000 watt, 4000 watt, 5000 watt, 8000 watt; usually interlocking dimmers in the 1000 watt to 5000 watt range.

b.   Dimmers are usually controlled by mechanically interlocked operating handles at knee level.

(1)   One master (sometimes two submasters) lever controls a shaft to which individual dimmers may be locked (by twisting the individual handle, a pin is dropped into a cam on the mastering shaft, locking the handle to the shaft).

c.   Knife switches are mounted over the dimmers and toward the back of the board; enclosed in sheet metal hinged cover, with switch operating handles projecting through slots in the cover.   Fuses are usually mounted on the switch blocks.

d.   Output pockets (usually stage connectors; sometimes pin connectors) are mounted at the top front of the board.

e.   Master switch (knife) mounted at one end, on the interior; serves as master disconnect and is used for blackout cues; contains board master fuses. Input to switch consists of three flexible leads with lugs for connection to company switch.

f.   Box is castered, constructed of wood and lined with sheet steel.   Weight is about 800 pounds.

g.   Board is usually provided with two, three, or four "hot pockets" for control of non-dim circuits; operating light is usually mounted in the board.

h.   Wiring is asbestos, single conductor.

i.   Ordinarily each professional company carries at least two boards; some productions have required as many as 12.

j.   Although such portable boards were originally designed for specific productions, the current practice is for a lighting supplier to rent or lease available boards and other lighting equipment to the production. Since the control board is not designed for the production and is often antiquated, the control problems are multitudinous. The "christmas tree" of portable stage cables branching out from the boards to the stage loads prevents operator visibility, and often interferes with control movements. That artistic lighting can be achieved under such adverse conditions is an indication of the devotion and diligence of professional lighting designers and electricians. Hopefully, the professional theatre will eventually be provided with alternating current, so that the designers and electricians can utilize control equipment capable of providing them with a system suitable to their talents.

2.   Package systems

Package systems are compact boxes containing six dimmers of ratings from 1000 watts to 6000 watts (usually one size of dimmer per package). The basic unit of six dimmers, with associated controls, fuses or breakers, output outlets or terminals, and supply leads, can be added to as the need and financial means allow. Package systems are available in the auto-transformer and solid-state types.

a.   Auto-transformer board

Contains six auto-transformer dimmers mounted in a compact box, with fuses or circuit breakers, control handles (the dial type of control has little application to stage lighting requirements), and output plugs. Proportional mastering requires an additional dimmer rated to carry the individual dimmers. Applicable where control requirements are minimal, and where the weight factor is not ciritcal. The Davis type auto-transformer dimmer allows electrical mastering, and provides some weight reduction, as well as size reduction.

b.   Solid-state package system

The solid-state package board is a highly flexible control unit, which provides a maximum of flexibility, with the inherent advantages of the solid-state dimmer: light weight, durable, dependable. The package contains 6 1800 to 6000 watt dimmers, case mounted. A control panel, which can be remotely located from the dimmer case, provides individual, and master dimming; two such control panels can be provided for two scene presetting. The system is provided with load connectors or terminals. This system is applicable to control requirements of the small to medium size installation (up to about thirty dimmers), requiring not more than two presets.

3.   Direct control systems

This type of control board has been used extensively where the lighting is standardized and arbitrary, and where the operator is limited as to authority.

a.   Load circuits are connected permanently to control circuits.

b.   Dimmers are usually mounted horizontally in banks corresponding to the various colors in the instruments, or corresponding to a definite arrangement of floor pockets in three or four colors.

c.   House light controls are usually grouped on one side of the board, and stage circuits on the other.

d.   All elements are arranged as compactly as possible, directly behind the dead face of the board, with each control unit containing dimmer, switch, and pilot light.

e.   Loads: Up to 3600 watts for plate dimmers, 8000 watts for auto-transformer dimmers. Higher load ratings can be accomplished with multiple units controlled by one dimmer handle.

f.   Interlocking is usually mechanical. Switching is sometimes provided for electrically mastering a group of individual dimmers on a higher capacity dimmer.

g.   Fuses or circuit breakers are placed in a magazine panel above, at the end, or behind the board.

h.   Contactor switching is sometimes provided for master switches; contactors are controlled by tumblers or toggles located on the control board; the contactors are placed in an isolated area, so that the noise of operation will not interfere with stage action.

i.   The control board is usually placed near the proscenium, stage right or stage left, frequently on a balcony.

j.   The direct control board provides very little flexibility; it consumes valuable stage space, and does not provide a great degree of operational ease. It should not be considered for installation.

4.   Direct control system with cross-connecting.

This system uses a control board similar to the direct control system with permanently connected loads. Although the system provides a greater degree of flexibility when the cross-connecting panel is used, thus permitting the connection of any load circuit to any dimmer, does not provide the operator visibility or ease of control possible with remote control systems. Although the use of auto-transformer dimmers instead of resistance dimmers provides multi-capacity control circuits, the problems of mechanical mastering and the limited visibility prevent the use of this type system where artistic lighting with a high degree of flexibility is to be attained.

5.   Remote control systems.

Remote control systems consist of a control console, a dimmer bank, and a cross-connecting panel. At the present time, this system utilizes either solid-state amplifier dimmers, magnetic amplifier dimmers, or tube dimmers.

a.   The dimmers, with associated power handling devices are located in a dimmer bank containing:

64

(1)   Dimmers, 1800-12000 watt ratings, mounted in plug-in chassis for easy maintenance, or replacement with a dimmer of different capacity rating.

(2)   Main contactor, rated at approximately 80% of total demand.

(3)   Panic contactors, usually 60A. to 100A. rating, mechanically held.

(4)   Non-dim contactors, usually 20A. to 100A. rating.

(5)   Transfer contactors (if dimmer control is transferred from stage to house loads; such transfer is often more economical than separate dimmers for house lighting).

(6)   Extended control contactors (if work lights are to be controlled from several positions about the stage or auditorium).

(7)   Power supplies for control and communication circuits.

(8)   Main and control fuses or circuit breakers.

b.   The cross-connecting panel is located on the stage, or in an accessible area near the stage and dimmer bank. The panel contains:

(1)   Dimmer and non-dim contactor output jacks, usually of the single conductor phone type. Two to eight jacks are provided for each control circuit, depending on the circuit rating.

(2)   Stage (load) circuit termination in phone type plugs; plugs are attached to flexible cords, usually weighted for retraction into the board.

(3)   Operating light and control switch are mounted on the panel.

(4)   The jack (control circuit) field is usually mounted on a vertical face; the plug (load circuit) field is usually mounted on a horizontal face.

(5)   Circuit breakers are provided for the load circuits, usually mounted on the bottom front of the board, sometimes on the end.

(6)   The cross-metering panel is sometimes used instead of the plugging arrangement. In this system, the horizontal bars are connected to the load circuits, and the vertical bars are connected to control circuits. The junctures are inter-connected by sliding connectors, allowing any load to be connected to any dimmer.

c.   The control console is located for maximum operator visibility, usually in a control booth at the back of the orchestra or first balcony. The control console contains:

(1)   Manual controls, one for each dimmer. These controls are usually designed for ease of operation: a small cross-section and finger fitting contour, with illuminated marking dial. These controls are used for the initial setting of readings, and for sight cues involving only one or two dimmers.

(2)   Once the cues have been set on the manual, the readings are transferred to the presets, either automatically, as in the punched data card system, or by transcription to small printed circuit preset cards. The preset controllers, if of the printed circuit or potentiometer type, are much smaller than the manual controllers, allowing for the compaction of controllers for all circuits into a small, easily handled unit. Preset banks may be made larger, and installed adjacent to the control console, if no more than ten presets are required. The plug-in card presetting arrangement is usually provided with plug-in mounting on the console for two to five such cards.

(3) Presets are energized by a fader, usually mounted on the desk surface of the console. The fader energizes one preset in the "up" position, and another preset in the "down" position. If more than two presets are to be alternately energized, a group of sequencing switches is provided for each position of the fader; one sequencing switch is provided for each position of the fader: if a preset switch is energized in the up group, that preset will be energized when the fader handle is moved to the up position; the energization will be transferred to the preset selected in the down position, when the fader handle is next moved to that position.

(4) The console contains switches, usually mounted in alignment with the manual controllers, for the transfer of control from the manual to the preset, thus allowing any dimmer circuit to be immediately transferred from preset to manual.

(5) The manual bank of controllers are provided with a manual master, allowing proportional dimming of all manual controls energized.

(6) A blackout selector is usually provided for the preset fader, so that the lights may fade to out before the fade up to the next preset.

(7) Controls are provided for house lighting circuits, for non-dim circuits, and for panic circuits.

(8) The control console should be equipped with two communication systems:

    (a) Constant communication with the stage manager, preferably a telephone type headset.

    (b) Emergency and maintenance communication with the stage manager, the cross-connecting panel, and the dimmer bank. This channel should use a sound powered handset, so as to operate in the event of power failure.

6. Load connected remote control systems.

The load connected remote control system utilizes small solid-state dimmers with 1800-6000 watt ratings located at the load. These dimmers are plugged into raceways containing line buses, and the load instruments are directly connected to the dimmer. Control wiring is provided from the dimmer to the control console. This system, operationally, is similar to the regular remote control system. Although the same degree and ease of flexibility is claimed, the primary advantage is one of cost. Although the dimmers can be moved from one location to another, moving a cross-connecting jack is much easier. The application of this type of system is on stages with little or no space available for the bank installation of dimmers and cross-connecting equipment.

V. PRINCIPLES OF DESIGN AND
ENGINEERING FOR THE CONTROL SYSTEM

The primary function of the lighting expert during the initial design period of a theatre is to advise the production organization and the architect as to budgetary and physical requirements of the lighting system. Once the initial design phase is completed and the preliminary budget is determined, the lighting expert uses these decisions as a basis for the selection, design, and engineering of the system components to provide a lighting system compatible with the requirements of the producing organization. In the process of resolving and co-ordinating architectural, budgetary, and production requirements, the lighting expert considers the expected use of the theatre and its lighting system in relation to: the type of production, the style of production, architectural requirements, and budgetary requirements. These considerations determine the size and general operational requirements of the lighting control equipment. The lighting expert then proceeds to design, select, and engineer the control system according to principles of control system design and engineering; these principles encompass the areas of human engineering, control engineering, safety engineering, and economy engineering.

A. HUMAN ENGINEERING

1. This category is the starting point for a design analysis of the lighting control system. Generally, the field of human engineering investigates the communication between operator and system: the relationship between operator and system: the relationship of the human being to the machine. The successful system or machine relieves the operator of routine tasks and allows the operator to direct the machine quickly and efficiently as to what operations are to be performed, when the operations are to be performed, and if necessary, provides a feedback information channel so that the operator is cognizant of the operational status of the system. The task of human engineering is to make the machine subordinate to and an extension of human capability, rather than restricting the human to the mechanical requirements of the machine.

2. The operator and his skills must be given due consideration in the design of a control system: control sophistication and flexibility must be geared to the ability and training of the operator. In a professional repertory situation, the control system might be more highly refined and might depend more on the training and knowledge of the operator; on the other hand, in an educational situation, where the ability and training of the operators vary widely, the control system must be more "fool-proof", and must compensate and automate to such an extent that operator failure or malfunction is minimized. Generally, educational situations should not attempt to gain ultimate flexibility, but should aim for straight-forward easily understood control routines and operations. It must be emphasized that there is no one ideal control system applicable to all production and control situations: every system must take into account the varying requirements, not the least of which is the skill, intelligence, training, and permanence of the operator.

3. The following items should be considered in an analysis of a lighting control system, and the final design should satisfy the requirements:

    a. Ease of operation: The human body is physically limited as to reach, comfortable working positions, strength, and psychological and physiological sensitivity.

        (1) Controls and displays (indicator elements) should be placed for operation from comfortable body positions. Elements which are most frequently used or require precise adjustment should be placed within optimum control zones, with elements requiring less precise adjustments and infrequent use placed in peripheral zones. Controls should be located so that the hand of the operator does not mask display devices when a control is manipulated.

        (2) Controller mechanical feedback (friction, detents, stops, etc.) should be sufficient to permit the operator to sense that the controller is moving as desired or is at the desired position.

    b. Visibility: The operator must be able to see what he is doing, and must be able to see the effects of his control manipulations.

        (1) Control position should be located so as to permit the operator a typical "audience" viewpoint. Sightlines should be such that the operator is not required to change his body position to see over the heads of the audience, or over the top of the control console. (Where sightline study is necessary, the minimum seat to eye dimension may be taken as 27 1/2", and the minimum seat to top of head distance as 40". Sightline angle should not exceed 30°.

        (2) Operating surfaces should be lighted so that the operator is not subjected to glare or confusing reflections. Panel areas surrounding critical display or control elements should be of a matte finish, with the surface of the controls brighter than the background.

        (3) The illumination level of the control area must be sufficiently low so as not to

require the operator's eyes to adapt from control surface brightness to stage surface brightness; where possible, operating lights should be provided with adjustable dimmer controls. Operating lights must be shielded so that they do not distract the audience's attention from the stage.

(4) All control elements should be logically arranged, clearly identified, and sufficiently spaced so that only a glance is necessary to identify the control or display device.

    (a) Controls should be placed close to their related displays, and should be arranged for area or group identification. Horizontal grouping is preferable to vertical grouping. Where necessary, provide a marked outline or colored background for each group, or mount each group on a differential plane.

    (b) Controls should be arranged for left to right operational sequence.

    (c) Pilot lamps should be used only where discrete qualitative (on-off, etc.) conditions are to be indicated. They must be of suitably low intensity so as not to distract or confuse the operator; suitable brightness is normally twice that of the background area. Pilot lamps which dim up and down (provide quantitative information) with control circuits are frequently confusing, and should be avoided. If intensity metering is necessary, use a graduated meter scale.

c. Human limitations:

(1) Controls and panels should be designed to fit the geometry and dimensions of the human body. Controls for hand operation should be located at a height between the elbow and shoulder of the operator, and within an arc of 28" measured from the shoulder. Controllers for foot operation should be generally avoided; if necessary, however, they should be located to provide a 120° angle between the upper and lower leg.

(2) Console dimensions should generally be as follows:

    (a) Operation from sitting position
        Height: (Horizontal surface) 29"
        Depth: (Horizontal surface) 12"-15"
        Sloping control surface at back of horizontal surface at 60° angle.

    (b) Operation from sit-stand (stool) position
        Height: (Horizontal surface) 37"-41"
        Depth: (Horizontal surface) 12"-15"
        Sloping control surface at back of horizontal surface at 45° angle.

    (c) Operation from standing position
        Height: (Horizontal surface) 37"-41"
        Depth: (Horizontal surface) 12"-15"
        Sloping control surface at back of horizontal surface at 30° angle.

(3) The control system should not require overly complicated movements or thought patterns of the operator. The human brain and body should be used primarily for decision making, not the performance of mere routine tasks. Where possible, machine operation and sequence should be automated so that the operator is free to attend to the job of integrating the lighting with the stage performance. However, the operator should not be permitted to become a purely passive element, required to function only when unusual conditions or emergency situations occur. If the operator has been passive under normal operational conditions, he more likely than not is out of touch with current system status, and conse-

quently does not have the necessary data to act intelligently in emergency situations. The operator must delegate sufficient monitoring and operational tasks so that he remains in touch with the status of the system. Habit reflex action permits quicker resolution of emergency situations.

4. Types, functions, and locations of control components.

   a. Read-in (controller) devices:

      (1) Controllers must maintain a compatible relationship with their movement and the controlled function (if the intensity of the light is to increase, the controller should move up or forward); controllers should be compatible with expected or usual relationships (a switch should be oriented so that down or toward the operator is off, and up or away from the operator is on.

      (2) Controller sizes:

         (a) Rotary continuous (analogue) controls should utilize a serrated round knob, 2" in diameter for critical adjustments, or 1" in diameter for less critical adjustments. Mechanical resistance should be approximately 2 inch pounds to provide proper "feel".

         (b) Digital (switching or stepping controls should utilize a bar pointer knob, with a mechanical resistance of approximately 8 inch pounds.

         (c) Linear controllers (most applicable to intensity controllers) should be not more than 7/8" in width, nor less than 1/4" in width. For manual operation where more than one controller is to be operated simultaneously, the width should be not less than 3/8", spaced on not less than 3/4" centers. Scale length should be not more than 10", nor less than 4 1/2". Mechanical resistance should be approximately 6 inch pounds.

         (d) Foot pedals should be pivoted at the heel, with spring tension supporting the weight of the operator's foot. Mechanical resistance should be approximately 20 inch pounds.

         (e) Toggle switches should operate at positions 30° to each side of center. Four to eight inch pounds force should be required to operate the switch.

         (f) Pushbuttons should be not less than 3/8" in diameter, and the surface should be concave in smaller diameters to fit the finger tip. Pressure for operation should not exceed 30 ounces; the finger should feel a definite click when the switch operates. Where accidental operation is possible, or where pushbuttons are closely spaced, barriers should be provided around each button, or buttons should be recessed in the mounting panel surface.

      (3) Controller positioning:

      Controllers should be located within limits as previously discussed; controllers for precise adjustments should be located to right of center if possible.

      (4) Controller coding:

         (a) Location coding should be used for group identification.

         (b) Shape coding is not generally recommended for lighting control systems.

         (c) Size coding may be used to identify similar control components within groups (master controller larger than submaster controllers, which are larger than individual controllers).

69

(d)   Color coding should be limited to red, blue, green, and amber when required to complement group or position coding. Do not use unless absolutely necessary, as color coding tends to become confused with color media in lighting instruments. Reserve red for emergency or panic controllers.

b. Read-out (indicator) devices:

(1)   Should be compatible with controller devices; if controllers are linear, indicators should be linear.

(2)   Circular (dial) scales provide a greater scale length in less space, however, these should be used only where rotary controllers are practical.

(3)   Moving pointers and fixed scales are generally preferable to fixed pointers and moving scales.

(4)   Scale marking or indexing should be limited to required accuracy of reading: the smallest marking or scale division should never be smaller than either the probable metering error or the smallest discernible effect in the controlled quantity (intensity of the light).

(5)   Counters may be used for digital readout. The numbers should snap into position to eliminate blur and reduce confusion. If consecutive reading is required, not more than two numbers per second should enter the visual field.

(6)   Pilot lights and warning light indicators may be used for display of discrete qualitative information. Lights should be approximately twice the brightness of the background, but should not be bright enough to impose confusing glare and contrast on the operator. Brightness and color are more important than size; color should be easily distinguishable, and should be related to colors used in controller coding where possible. Warning lights should be mounted within 30° of the operator's visual axis; a flashing light may be used if signal is not within the visual range (flash rate should be 3-10 flashes per second, with a flash duration of not less than .05 seconds.

c. Lettering, marking, and numbering of control components:

(1)   Caps should be used for identification labelling of control components; caps with lower case should be used for supplementary or instructional labelling.

(2)   Labels should read from left to right horizontally; up to down vertical labels should be used only where crowding and confusion would result from horizontal labelling.

(3)   Lettering and numerals should have no flourishes, but should be simple and prominent. Engraved lettering should be used wherever possible.

(4)   Stroke width of black letters on white background should be 1/6 the character height; stroke width of white letters on black background should be 1/8 the character height. Height to width ratio of letters should be 3.2; space between characters should be equal to one stroke width, and spaces between words should be equal to one character width.

(5)   The distance between scale markings should be not less than twice the stroke width of the markings. Major markings or numbered indices should be spaced approximately 1/2" apart, with not more than 10 divisions between numbered indices. Major marks or indices should be slightly heavier than smaller scale divisions.

(6) Scale pointers should be close to the scale marking, but should never cover the marking or the number. Scale marking and pointer should not be spaced more than 1/16" apart. The pointer should be mounted to avoid misreading due to parallax; pointer should be of the same color as the scale markings, and should be of simple design.

(7) All figures and letters should be placed vertically.

(8) On finite scales, there should be a break larger than one major scale division between the end and the beginning of the scale.

(9) Where figures or markings are to be read through a window opening, two or more figures should appear in the window at any one time.

(10) The best scale progression for stage lighting intensity is 0-10, with numerals at each digit position, secondary markings at mid-points between numerals, and the smallest scale markings at 1/4 positions between digit positions.

(11) All scale divisions should be of equal length. Although the recommended dimming curve follows the square output law, control circuitry should be compensated to provide such a curve at equal scale divisions.

d. Auditory equipment may be used either as (1) warning and signalling devices to inform the operator of a control state or function; such signals allow the operator to be cognizant of a control function with being visually oriented toward the source of the signal; or (2) communication devices between two or more operators. Handheld communication equipment should be used only if the operator is free to use a hand to operate and support the handset; otherwise, head-supported equipment should be used. If the control console is located in a sound-proof booth, loudspeaker intercommunication equipment should be used for normal communication. Emergency sound-powered handset communication equipment should be provided from the console to the stage manager, the amplifier dimmer bank, and the patch panel.

B. CONTROL ENGINEERING

Control engineering is concerned with the technical fulfillment of the system design requirements. After the size of the control system, the extent of automation, and the operational requirements have been determined, the system should be engineered to meet the following requirements:

1. Dependability: One of the foremost requirements of any control system is that it perform the job it is designed to do with a minimum of attention and a minimum of failure. In any complex control system, a certain amount of component failure must be expected; such failure should be reduced to a practical minimum, and the system should be so designed that, should a failure occur, it can be corrected quickly and easily, either automatically, or by the operator. Most commercially available control systems are dependable if competently installed and maintained; irritating failures are all too frequently the result of improper or complete lack of routine maintenance. Although dependability is difficult to predict when reading specifications or looking at equipment, it is frequently indicated by the quality of the components and their installation. If carefully selected components of reputable manufacture are used throughout the system, if the assembly and wiring are logical and neat, the system is probably dependable. If, however, other than first quality components and materials are apparent, if assembly and wiring are haphazard or shoddy, or if components are "sealed" and inaccessible for inspection, it is quite possible that failure might occur at an inopportune time. If defects are apparent, or concealment and inaccessibility of components for inspection are apparent, the manufacturer should be questioned.

2. Flexibility: A suitable control system is designed and engineered to allow the achievement of varying control requirements. The system should be sufficiently flexible to con-

trol varying loads, and allow grouping flexibility for operational ease. Dimmers should be multi-capacity in most instances, and of a sufficient capacity rating to handle the expected loads. Load circuits should be distributed about the stage for expected instrument arrangement; usually load circuits should be terminated at a patch or cross-connecting panel. If, however, the system is to be used in a fixed load and control situation, such patching flexibility will only contribute to the cost, not to the usefulness of the system. Dimmers should respond to control operations in not more than 1/4 of a second (15 cycles response time).

C. SAFETY ENGINEERING

The control system should be designed and engineered so that it presents no mechanical or electrical hazards to personnel. The system and its components should be arranged and protected to provide electrical isolation of all surfaces and parts which might be touched by any person. A grounding system should be incorporated in all equipment so that a failure of electrical insulation will not permit an electrical potential to be placed on cabinets or other exposed surfaces. Cabinets, racks, raceways, and conduits should be of sufficient structural strength to prevent damage to electrical conductors by falling objects. Heavy equipment should be installed on adequate structural supports. Generally, equipment which conforms with the requirements of a recognized testing laboratory (such as Underwriters Laboratories) and the requirements of the National Electrical Code, may be considered as safe. It should be noted, however, that UL approval or conformance with code requirements does not imply suitable performance characteristics.

D. ECONOMY ENGINEERING

The goal of economy engineering is to ascertain which of equivalent solutions is the most feasible and least expensive in terms of both initial and subsequent (operational and maintenance) costs. Usually there is more than one way of accomplishing any control function; the technique which provides the required function (while fulfilling the requirements for dependability, safety, etc.) at the lowest total cost is usually the best choice. In analyzing the economy of a solution, the situation should be reduced to the simplest possible statement of the operation or function to be performed (verb and noun: dimmer "changes intensity"). Once the basic function and requirements are established, alternative solutions should be considered; oftimes an unnecessary process or stage can be eliminated during such an analysis, or an entirely different approach may be recognized as a simpler solution. Generally, the least complex and most straight-forward approach is the best solution to a control problem. All too often the attempt to achieve flexibility is allowed to overshadow the basic and immediate control requirement, thus resulting in a flexible system which is much too complex and complicated to be used efficiently and much too expensive to be justified by normal usage.

In summary, the lighting control system should be designed to suit the requirements of the producing organization, to co-ordinate with the architectural design, and to comply with the budgetary allotment. Once the basic layout has been determined, the control equipment should be engineered to meet the requirements of the operator and relieve him of routine tasks; to be safe and dependable; and to be economical in cost, operation, and maintenance.

4. LAYOUT

Instruments and control are valuable only to the extent that they are incorporated successfully in the special plan of the theatre. This includes the structural elements, wiring, number and proportion of types of instruments, type of control, and various accessories which are determined by the methods of production.

The theatre is a special instrument designed and constructed within practical limits for dramatic production. The diversity of conditions determining the plan limits standardization and makes the design of each theatre a special problem. The proper selection and coordination of parts provide a freedom from technical limitations and tend to stimulate the use of light as a dramatic medium beyond its conventional use as a medium to give visibility. Technical limitations invariably determine the extent of expression with light and thereby establish somewhat the style of production. This selection of equipment and the arrangement of structural plans should be based upon the ultimate demands of production. A layout which is slavishly based upon the past is bound to continue many limitations which should be overcome.

I. ITEMS GOVERNING THE DESIGN OF THE LAYOUT

In order to achieve results with equipment, flexibility of space and apparatus and the determination of methods of application based on the purpose for which the theatre is to be used, must be considered as elements which dictate the design. Obviously, the layouts of a laboratory or school theatre, repertory or permanent-company theatre, arena theatre, motion-picture theatre, the symphony auditorium and the recital stage or the outdoor theatre, have different purposes which dictate the extent and type of layout. For each one of these the problem of site, budget, the number of seats, variety of purposes, concept of the architect, and the solution of structural details are practical elements that govern the final solution. In general, the following items should be considered in the determination of the layout for each of the above purposes.

A. PURPOSE OF EQUIPMENT IN THE THEATRE

Equipment is only a means to an end. It is much more desirable that the operator be forced to be ingenious with a limited equipment which he knows thoroughly than to be governed by a layout which seems to be an end in itself and portions of which are used only at very rare intervals. The equipment which is most suited to the problem allows for the most subtle use of light. Many times special positions and instruments justify their installation for a specific purpose, but generally the layout should be sufficiently flexible to serve for any purpose. The functions of light serve as the basic guide.

B. METHODS OF LIGHTING DETERMINING THE SELECTION OF INSTRUMENTS

Although each type of production demands a different range of expression of the qualities of light, practice has indicated that certain groups of instruments can be classified according to the purpose they serve.

1. Auditorium Lights. Open or concealed fixtures for giving visibility and under certain conditions, creating atmosphere. Illumination of the seating area by direct lighting. Toning of the auditorium for atmosphere by indirect light, sometimes in three colors. Patterns of light as in the atmospheric theatre. Exit lights and sometimes aisle lights are an essential part of the layout.

2. Acting Area Lights. Generally a group of spotlights controlled separately to cover the acting areas of the stage. Six conventional areas, two serving each area. Range of intensity and color. Ceiling beams, side slots, balcony, bridge or first pipe, and tormentors.

3. Toning and Blending Mediums. Footlights, controlled in three or four colors, sometimes in sections. Border lights used as blending mediums, controlled in three or four circuits, sometimes in two or three sections.

73

4. Background Lights. High-powered instruments used above the stage to illuminate the cyclorama or back drop, in three or more colors, generally one section. Horizon lights in three or four colors, sometimes in three sections. Backing lights and ground row lights.

5. Special Lights. Motivating lights, entrance lights, and decorative effects, fed from floor pockets, the bridge, and the gridiron.

C. FLEXIBILITY OF SPACE AND EQUIPMENT

The diversity of the demands placed upon the average stage for the presentation of various types of productions with their accompanying lighting distributions, indicates that there should be considerable flexibility in the use of instruments and structural elements.

1. Unobstructed Space. The stage is a space into which light is projected. Any temporary structural features can be built in. Even the auditorium should be considered as a mechanical part of the stage, inasmuch as the light should be thrown on the stage from that direction, and in some cases the various distributions of light from the house lights can be relied upon to create an atmosphere surrounding the audience.

   a. Simplification of the auditorium. Decoration of the auditorium in harmony with the stage picture.

   b. Balcony when over 700 seats are needed.

   c. The size of the stage and the proscenium. Up to 400 seats—24' x 14'; 400 to 1000—30' x 16'; 1,000 to 2,000—35' x 24'; 2,000 to 3,000—40' x 30'. Minimum dimensions.

   d. The size of the stage and the relation of the auditorium to it: depth equal to the width of the proscenium, twice as wide, three times as high. Minimum dimensions.

2. Flexibility of Equipment. Based upon the methods of lighting, certain instruments should be portable so as to be used in a number of places. As a principle, only the instruments necessary for the direct use of light as a part of the production should be provided. Portability stimulates the selection of the proper layout of instruments.

   a. Standardized hangings and connections.

   b. Structual details such as beam openings, balcony front hoods, bridges, etc.

   c. Special instruments, footlights, cyclorama lights, etc., designed for a definite purpose sometimes portable. Space occupied may be used for other purposes.

   d. Adequate wiring and number of outlets at important positions.

D. DIVISION OF BUDGET

It is impossible to make any definite suggestion as to the divisions of the budget for a building. Yet the following suggestions are offered as a guide to the various amounts that should be allowed for lighting under any conditions. Ordinarily the architect and the owner treat the lighting budget as a flexible element to be used to absorb the extras in the other phases of installation and construction, whereas even in the beginning an insufficient allowance is usually provided for an adequate lighting layout. These estimates are based on the budget of a laboratory or experimental theatre.

1. Perhaps 12% of the total cost of the building should be assigned to the electrical and lighting layout for the entire building. It should be less for very large buildings and perhaps as high as 20% for small, cheaply constructed buildings.

2. Of this 12% approximately 30-50% should go to the switchboard; 15-25% to instruments and accessories, 25-45% to the structural features, the wiring, and the rest of the electrical layout.

74

II. PRACTICAL ELEMENTS

Restating the above in practical terms, the following details are submitted as a guide, but not as a rule. Each type of theatre, as well as each type of production, requires an analysis of the problem in order to arrive at an economical layout. The wiring to positions for serving the various types of instruments, their number and type, the control board, signal system, and accessories such as cycloramas or domes, are the essential parts of any layout.

A. WIRING

The main distribution board provides service for general lighting of the building. The stage, exit and emergency lighting, and power. The building Code dictates standard practice for wiring.

1. <u>General Service.</u> Lobbies, offices, rest rooms, corridors, shops, dressing rooms, and so on.

2. <u>Exit Lights.</u> All exit lights, inside and out, and in the corridors where the fixture is equipped with an extra circuit, separately fused and connected ahead of the main disconnect switch on the distribution board; connected also to an auxiliary service or an emergency M.G. set.

3. <u>Auxiliary Service and Panic Lights.</u> Sometimes service from another power plant or a motor generator provided as part of the equipment of the building. Usually this service feeds only small sources in auditorium, the corridors, lobbies, and exit lights. Automatic throw-over switch. Emergencies.

4. <u>The Stage.</u> Stage mains (110 volts) running to main contactor panel or directly to the magazine panel in the switchboard. 3 or 4 wire alternating current. D.C. service for arcs. Picture-booth service generally requires D.C., A.C. can be converted into D.C. by a motor generator or rectifier. About 1 1/2-3 amperes per square foot of proscenium opening can be used as an estimate of the total stage load for a legitimate theatre.

   a. Feeds both stage and house lights. Fused in each step and each branch circuit.

   b. Special wiring for different types of boards, portable, permanent, and flexible.

   c. Distribution from switchboard to house lights, stage outlets, and fixed instruments through conduit or portable leads. Plugging boxes.

   d. Stage floor outlets generally of the arc pocket type, 50-ampere capacity. Incandescent pockets can be standardized in 15-ampere pin connector or 20-ampere twistlock female outlets. Mounted at the ends of pigtails or along the length of a permanently-mounted wire-way, on bridges, borders, and tormentors or in floor pockets.

   e. Large flexible, multiconductor, multicapacity marine cable from gridiron or side wall, suitably supported to relieve strain. Outlets mounted on a pipe equipped with strain insulators. Slack supported by saddles connected to steel batten cables or handled individually by a counterweight system.

   f. Fixed instruments such as borders and footlights connected permanently to the feed service through junction boxes.

   g. Portable instruments fed by long length of cable with a plug or male pin connector, but generally short pigtails with male connectors. A continuous strip of portable sections fed through male pin connectors at one end of each section and female pin connector outlets at the opposite end.

   h. The company switch. For traveling shows and also where there is a demand for extra control. Large capacity. Mounted near to the proscenium on either side of the stage. 1/2 to 3/4 of the capacity of a house board.

i.   Signal system. See "G" in this section.

B.   POSITIONS FOR OUTLETS

Outlets should be provided in number and capacity at convenient positions, based on the methods of lighting, to serve a practical number of instruments. The elimination of long portable leads is desirable. (The standardization as far as possible of short standard lengths of portable cable, equipped with 20-ampere male connector on one end and female on the other.) Built-in traps, hanging battens, and bridges are useful for mounting lights so that they can be directed from a number of positions. Portable battens, stands, bridges, towers, and so on are useful to allow variety of mounting positions in the stage space. Instruments should be equipped with pipe clamps and swing joints to allow hanging in a number of positions and focusing in desired directions, depending upon the purpose for which they are generally used. The following details indicate the various positions to take into consideration.

1.   Projection Booth. Two projection-machine outlets. D.C., independent of stage. Two D.C. outlets for arc spots. Wiring for sound effects. Telephone and signal or Public Address (P.A.) connection with the stage. 50 A. for inc. follows.

2.   House Lights. Direct and indirect controlled in several circuits from the stage board. Exit and aisle lights. A panic circuit controlled from the booth and stage manager's desk can throw on a portion of the house lights in case of fire or other emergency. Cleaning lights controlled from stage manager's desk and rear of house. (key switch).

3.   Balcony Rail. Two to twelve 15 or 20-ampere outlets. Provision for remote color control. Housing for the instrument. Center and ends of balcony. Used to flood front of stage. Danger of shadows because of low angle. Take place of beam and side lights, or used in conjunction with them. Good for flooding curtain and orchestra or for front lighting for the chorus in musical shows.

4.   Beam, Ceiling, or Front Lights. Four to twelve outlets, depending upon the length and angle of throw and desired flexibility of control. Provision for remote color and directional control. Angle of throw approximating the diagonal of the cube. If possible, allow for the use of more than one beam position to vary the vertical angle from 35 to 75 degrees. Construction of ceiling beams to house the instrument and the use of funnels or mats to prevent spill of light into the auditorium. Provision of adjustable hanging and mounting apparatus. Provision of covers to close openings when not used; screens when they are. Used to illuminate the front of acting area and act curtain. High-wattage spotlights or projectors. Position concealed from the auditorium. Telephone or signal connections if operators are used.

5.   Side Lights. Generally used if there are no balcony rail or beam lights. Mounted in slots or turrets on vertical pipe battens. Good for low angle side lights to take the place of tormentor units.

6.   Orchestra Lights. Convenience outlets in the floor of the orchestra pit to serve orchestra stands. Separate circuit for leader. Night light circuit.

7.   Footlights. Direct-indirect, permanent, portable, and disappearing. Wired for three or four colors, and several sections. Shorter than the proscenium is wide. If divided into three parts, center section as long as two ends together. Provision for three or four outlets for footlight spots in presentation houses.

8.   Bridge (generally only one) See First Border. Hung directly upstage from the act drop or the teaser. Approximately as long as the proscenium is wide. Mounting provisions from the rail or underneath by two or three fixed battens. Access doors. Adjustable heights. Ten to twenty outlets, grouped or spread along wire-way with long pigtails. Approach by rope ladder or tormentor towers. Stays and outriggers. Two to four arc outlets for effects. Provision for remote color and directionality control. Signal or telephone to stage manager.

9. Perches or Side Galleries. On both sides of the stage. Perches from ten to fifteen feet above the stage floor near the proscenium, access by iron ladder. Side Galleries from fifteen to twenty-five feet above the stage. Mounting Rail and continuous wire-way with four to eight long pigtails to feed either perch or gallery.

10. Tormentors. Four to twelve pigtail outlets on each side of the stage, attached to proscenium wall or grouped along portable wire-way. Towers with operating platforms. Adjustable proscenium with the teaser thickness piece. Ladder and portable outlet wire-way.

11. First Border. Used in case there is no bridge, or as additional outlets just upstage from the bridge. Four to twelve outlets on a pipe batten, hung from strain insulators; or a permanent strip wired for three or four colors, fed by cable suspended from the grid or from side wall. Asbestos shield to keep instruments from burning cloth teaser. Lower teaser trim than with bridge and thickness piece.

12. Additional Borders. Conventional distance seven feet apart, for the rest of the depth of the stage. Four to eight circuits, fed by cable supported from the grid; outlets or fixed strips. Draped curtain or wing and border sets should have a strip behind each cloth border.

13. Grid Outlets. Outlets mounted on the grid to serve special instruments wherever they may be hung or spotted.

14. Cyclorama Lights. Three to nine large-capacity circuits supplying the overhead cyclorama units. In a position where they are apt to be most generally used. Fed by cable suspended from the grid. Special counterweight to take up slack as instruments are raised.

15. Floor Pockets. Outlets mounted in a box equipped with a self-closing lid, under the stage floor. Spaced around the sides and rear of the acting area. Generally of the 50-ampere plug pocket type, although better for standard connections of the 15-ampere pin-connector type. Three, or four, outlets in each box. Sometimes controlled in pairs, one on each side of the stage and given a color name such as red, blue, etc. The number of outlet boxes varies with the conditions of use, from three to twelve. Arc and incandescent pockets identified or in separate boxes. To serve stand-lamps, towers, or stage fixtures and special effects. Special traps and outlets for horizon strips. Three to four color sections. Portable type can be fed from up-stage floor pockets.

C. WORK LIGHTS.

Work lights are only used to illuminate the stage during rehearsal and for changing scenery. They should be operated from the switchboard or stage manager's desk, under instant control for resetting the stage when the curtain comes down. Usually this is the only use for fixed strips in the average theatre.

1. Work lights can be attached to any of the existing circuits or run independently for the stage area.

2. Sometimes two or three units on an independent circuit in permanent strips.

3. First border or bridge on the side walls, and upstage. Up-and-down distribution.

4. Operating lights for switchboard, pin rail, prompt board, and orchestra lights controlled from separate panel of mercury switches. No spill.

5. Rehearsal lights are special instruments used to light the acting area during rehearsal. Controlled from the stage manager's desk. Generally two projector floods mounted in the ceiling beams and two down floods mounted on the bridge can serve to provide adequate illumination. (The latter are used for work lights also.)

D. INSTRUMENTS. See Appendix V.

The available stock instruments and accessories that go with them can be selected as the special demands and methods of lighting dictate. The number of each type depends upon the methods outlined in Section I, Paragraph B, of this chapter. As an example, the layout for a stage with a proscenium 28' x 16' is given. For an average layout, the following schedule of equipment indicates the instruments required to give a reasonable and flexible layout. The budgetary divisions are included to show the relative importance of the number and type of each instrument. All instruments are portable and can be used in places other than those suggested. Prices are those applicable in 1964. Lamps, color frames, cables, and stands are included.

FIRST $1500

1. Two 8-foot sections of borderlights using 150-300 watt reflector lamps and glass roundels. These are wired in four colors and used to tone the acting area. They are hung from the first border pipe or bridge and equipped with end-studs, arms, and pipe clamps. Both ends are equipped with pigtails and connectors for feeding the second strip through the first.

2. Six fresnel spotlights of the 250-500-750 watt size, with a 6 x 3 1/2 lens. These are used to light the acting area and are hung from the first border pipe or bridge, or in the tormentor, and are equipped with a yoke and pipe clamp.

3. Six ellipsoidal-reflector spotlights of the 250-500-750 watt size, with either two 6 x 9 lenses (for distances up to 25 feet) or one 8 x 10 lens (for distances 25 to 40 feet). Used to light the acting area from the ceiling beams or other front-of-the-house location, and are equipped with framing shutters, yoke, and pipe clamp.

4. Two ellipsoidal spotlights of the 250-500-750 watt size, with two 6 x 9 lenses. For accenting areas or objects, or other special purposes.

SECOND $1500

5. One 8-foot and two 4-foot sections of footlights, using 150 watt reflector lamps. Wired in four colors with pigtails at both ends, equipped with end studs, to be mounted in the footlight trough.

6. Two 6-foot striplights and four 4 1/2-foot striplights, using 150 or 300 watt reflector lamps on 6-inch centers and equipped with colored spread roundels. Wired in three colors with pigtails at both ends, end-studs and legs mounted on a base or a rolling truck. For lighting the cyclorama from the bottom.

THIRD $1500

7. Four 9-inch ellipsoidal etched aluminum floods using a 100 watt A lamp or a 250-400 watt G lamp. Used for flooding broad surfaces at close range and for lighting entrances. Equipped with a swing-joint and arm. Four adjustable floor stands, 5 to 8 feet high, with heavy bases.

8. Two 8-foot and six 4-foot reflector lamp strips, using 300 watt reflector lamps and spread colored glass roundels. Wired for four colors, pigtails at both ends. Equipped with end-studs, arms, and pipe clamps. Reflector spill shields may be added later. For lighting the upper portion of the cyclorama from overhead.

FOURTH $1500

9. Four 6-foot striplights, as those in 6. For lighting ground rows, etc., or extended wings of the cyclorama.

10. Four fresnel spotlights with 8 x 4-3/4 lens, using a 1000-1500 G-40 lamp. Equipped with

yoke and pip-clamp. Four 10-foot stands on casters. Used to give high-intensity soft-edged beam as for sunlight and moonlight.

11.   Four 6-inch fresnel spotlights, as those in 2. For special accenting or fill light.

12.   Two ellipsoidal-reflector spotlights, similar to those in 4, but with 4 1/2 x 3 1/2 stepped lens. For special accenting, side lighting, etc.

FIFTH $1500

13.   One effect machine with three objectives of different focal length lens combinations.

14.   Two small Linnebach projectors, using 1000-watt lamp.

15.   A collection of accessories such as extra lamps, cable, color frames, color mediums, lenses, hangers, funnels, stands, framing shutters, glass roundels, and towers.

16.   A supply of onstage fixtures such as brackets, chandeliers, fire-logs, fire grates, and various effects, as water ripples, moving clouds, etc.

17.   Additional equipment to be ordered as the demand is created. Generally it is cheaper to rent than to keep on hand a quantity of instruments that are seldom used.

E. CONTROL BOARD

A switchboard designed to give the greatest flexibility of control in view of the purpose for which the building is designed. It is the most important item in the whole layout. The position of the board depends upon its type and the purpose for which it is designed. Consoles should invariably be placed out front. All house lights and stage lights should be controlled from this board.

F. COMPANY SWITCH

Large-type safety service switch may be mounted adjacent to the proscenium on stage-left or -right, equipped with clamps to take the lugs at the ends of the feeds if any portable board is to be used. Capacity large enough to serve all the stage instruments apt to be brought in by a traveling company. 500-2000 amperes.

G. SIGNAL SYSTEM

Prompt Board, or Stage Manager's Desk. On account of the size of the ordinary theatre building and the necessity of dispatch in performance, communication between all individuals connected with production should be available to the stage manager. All parts of the stage, dressing rooms, and all parts of the building used in connection with a performance are important positions to be considered. Methods of production determine the type of signal board that should be provided. The prompt board should have a well-shielded operating light and should be placed near the proscenium. Signals may operate on low voltage.

H. SCENIC EQUIPMENT

Cycloramas, domes, gauzes, translucent screens, picture screens and scenery can be considered as secondary instruments, which, fixed or portable, serve as a part of the complete equipment of any stage.

1.   Cycloramas. Used as background for the stage. Generally to represent sky, although cycloramas painted with landscapes are sometimes used. If without wrinkles, with a perfectly flat painted surface, and evenly lighted, it gives an absolute illusion of distance. Projections of clouds or irregular lighting tend to destroy the illusion of distance.

   a.   A smooth surface in a large sweeping curve; elliptical half-cylinder with splayed sides the usual type. Should reach down-stage to the sight-lines at the proscenium, or tormentors. High enough to mask the sight-lines under the teaser or high masking border. Best when covered with a light blue scrim.

b. Built either permanently of plaster or profile board, or cloth. Flying side tabs, which lap slightly the front edge of a solid, fixed portion permit quick shift. The shape of a solid cyclorama should be designed to satisfy acoustical requirements. Cross-over from one side of the stage to the other should be provided. The cloth flying type requires a high grid. Battens on top and bottom, laced on. Wide widths of cloth, (linen or velour) best sewn vertically to avoid seam wrinkles. Battened and laced top and bottom. Adequate clearing space below when cyclorama is up.

c. German type rolling cyc for large stages. Overhead curved track; sometimes two or three; generally white and a dark blue, which use the same track, one at each end. Roll into a vertical cylinder by means of motor. Do not require bottom batten or extra height to grid for fly space. Painted to prevent small wrinkles.

d. Traveling cyc. Generally hung from straight rear batten and side legs with curved arm at the point where the two join. Not effective from the standpoint of illusion. In order to fold for shipping it must be colored with dye.

e. On shallow stages, cycloramas should be colored a light gray-blue. On large stages, the best flexibility in color change can be obtained with a perfectly white surface. Surface should be absolutely diffusing. Flat color for solid cycloramas to avoid specular reflection.

2. Domes. Used similarly to cycloramas for masking and the creation of illusion of sky. Valuable for arbitrary effects. Danger of acoustic problems. Useful only where there is little overhead space.

a. Shaped generally in the form of a quarter-sphere to cover sight-lines. Shape could consider the distribution of available light instruments used for its illumination and acoustical requirements.

b. Eliminates a certain amount of overhead hanging space but complicates the problem of flying scenery.

c. Should be formed to allow greatest setting space on stage as far away from the acting area as possible.

d. Best color flat white; but generally spill light makes night skies impossible with a white surface, so that a gray-blue (perhaps stippled) is generally more practical. Should allow for a complete range of color over its surface.

3. Gauzes. Used generally across the stage parallel to the proscenium to give the illusion of distance or to decrease the visibility of objects behind them. If illuminated equally over the entire surface from the front or back with a sheet of light which does not illuminate anything else, it acts as a film over whatever might be seen behind it. Dimming up lights behind the gauze illuminates objects which have hitherto been unseen. Use a black curtain directly behind the gauze for complete obliteration before objects are to be seen behind it. Gauze is sometimes called "scrim" or "transparency."

Several gauzes can be used parallel to each other to increase the sense of depth. Not visible if not lighted, but objects behind them are. The use of more than one gauze will cause a watermark effect unless they are different sized mesh or hung far apart.

a. The gauze can be dyed or painted to match the surrounding surfaces in pattern or in flat color. Generally it appears darker than the surrounding surfaces.

b. It picks up stray light easily and cannot be projected through for lighting objects behind, except with general illumination.

    c.   The gauze should be continuous over the entire opening. It is very fragile and cannot be patched easily. Ordinarily it must be stretched tightly to remove wrinkles. It can be used for decorative effects in draped folds.

    d.   The colors are generally dark, medium and light blue. White is not practical because it picks up too much light. The size of the thread and closeness of the weave determines transparency.

4.   <u>Translucent Screens</u>. A large sheet which allows transmission of light from behind without disclosing the light source.

    a.   Should be seamless. Shellacked, gelatined, rubberized, plasticized or dampened muslin. The best screens are of a plastic or cellulose material and are of the type used in making process shots in the motion pictures.

    b.   Partially translucent back drops with opaque patterns allow for changing effects when lighted from both front and back. Water and sky with opaque horizon. Clouds for a sunset.

5.   <u>Scenery, Costumes and Make-up.</u> All objects on stage have to be illuminated to be seen. Certain lighting effects can be obtained through the use of standard instruments and well-designed scenery much more readily than others. No effect is entirely satisfactory unless allowance is made for the combination of instruments given, particularly the direction and the color that must be used with relation to the motivation called for in the manuscript of the play.

    a.   The shape, texture, mounting position and pigment should be chosen in consideration of the light that is to be used.

    b.   Curtain sets. Complete set of wings and travellers to mask entire stage.

    c.   Unit sets should be adjustable and painted a neutral color; made up, perhaps, of a gray ground-coat and stippled with the three secondaries, magenta, yellow, and cyan blue, to allow greatest variety in selective reflection to the primary colors of the tonal lighting.

III. TYPES OF THEATRES

The divergent purposes and methods of production for which the various types of theatres are designed and built permits only approximate classification into types. Obviously, the equipment varies according to purpose, and the following discussion is only an attempt to analyze the equipment layouts as they throw a relatively different emphasis upon the foregoing practical suggestions. The ability to evaluate this relative importance will guarantee the most practical design of the layout for each type of theatre.

A.   HISTORY

The picture-frame stage with the wings and borders and small strips of lamps still influence our methods of production more than we realize. The belief in realism continues to dominate the average playwright. Unconsciously, he feels that this is the only sure means of conveying his idea to an audience. The motion-picture theatre, on the other hand, has had a tremendous influence in educating the audience to the wonders and dramatic possibilities of arbitrily-used lighting. The development of college and university theatres and some community plants on a scale, often exceeding the layout of the professional theatre, have had considerable influence in making the theatre building a useful and more effective instrument for the production of plays. Architects are becoming aware of the existence of certain theatres which serve their functions more successfully than the average and that these are the ones which should serve as a precedent. The mistakes and failures in the planning of the theatres today, as well as the good points, are the result of all these influences.

B. LABORATORY OR SCHOOL THEATRE (ARENA, SIDE STAGES, ETC.)

This is a building devoted to research, experimentation and professional practice which is operated by a permanent staff. The variety in the types of production and the flexibility in the use of equipment require perhaps the most careful consideration in planning a layout. No completely satisfactory solution has been found for reducing the effect of scale in a large auditorium designed for musical productions and large convocations, to the more intimate atmosphere consistent with dramatic production. The cost of setting for the more experimental types of production which must be easily staged, indicates that a small auditorium (400-700 seats) is most desirable for strictly experimental purposes. But in each case the stage should be thoroughly equipped and there should be additional laboratories, shops, studios, classrooms, and rehearsal rooms incorporated in the building. See Section II of this chapter.

C. REPERTORY COMMUNITY OR PERMANENT-COMPANY THEATRE

This is a building such as the Europeans call the theatre, used constantly for performances which change weekly or even twice daily. Here it is practical to mount the instruments more or less permanently and in such a quantity that a reasonable flexibility of light distribution can be obtained. Usually there is a permanent staff and light plots have been previously arranged. This type of theatre covers the ordinary legitimate repertory, but the classification can be extended to cover the opera and presentation houses. In these cases, standardization has reached a very high point and the use of light as an arbitrary medium of decoration, rather than as a means to create dramatic effect, allows for considerable simplification over the type of layout that might be found in the experimental theatre.

1. The number of outlets and the means of control should allow for as great flexibility as the experimental theatre, although practice seems to indicate that it is more practical to provide for the permanent connection of a number of instruments and the use of a more or less standardized method of lighting.

2. Remote color control and focusing, the use of glass color mediums and structural arrangements such as adjustable proscenium light towers, bridges, etc., allow for making the set-up for each new production rapidly.

3. Curtain sets and cloth borders (the average high school stage scenic equipment) require a strip light behind each border. There should be additional outlets for spotlights (on the first border at least) and floor pockets to feed side towers of spots or floods.

D. THE RENTED THEATRE

This is the usual type of professional theatre, being given over to visiting companies for motion pictures, presentations, musical shows, legitimate performances, and operas. All means of illuminating the stage space must be provided by the visiting company.

1. The house switchboard controls the house lights and footlights and borders, if any.

2. Work lights, floor pockets, hanging battens, and a signal system are generally provided, although few of them are used at any one time.

3. A company switch mounted near the proscenium serves the portable board which is brought in with the rest of the lighting equipment. 1 1/2 to 3 amps. per square foot of proscenium opening.

E. GENERAL PURPOSE AUDITORIUMS

This is generally a large auditorium with a reasonably confined stage. Due to the diversity of types of production for which this type of theatre is used, the flexibility generally occurs in the house or auditorium lighting rather than on the stage. This is the type of stage that is ordinarily provided by the architect for high schools and community houses. Insofar as the stage equipment and space are limited, the effectiveness of legitimate productions is likewise limited.

1. Often a large apron, little or no offstage space, and generally no overhead space.

2. Generally there is an elaborate lighting system for the auditorium, such as might be used to help create various atmospheric effects, not only for the different types of productions, but perhaps to help enhance the reception of music. This demands the use of a more elaborate type of switchboard than is necessary where the lighting serves the purpose of mere illumination.

3. Where there is no overhead space, it is often desirable to use a dome on the stage and to provide special means of lighting the orchestra from concealed sources.

F. OUTDOOR THEATRE

Due to the variety in type and scale of these productions, it is difficult to suggest any definite form of lighting layout. In general, productions must of necessity be somewhat more arbitrary in their effects, and the use of light to create naturalistic effects is correspondingly limited. The pageant form, whether it be an actual pageant, an intimate play, or an operatic production, presents much the same problem. Generally the area to be covered and the light-absorbing quality of the natural background require a much greater quantity of light than is necessary on the indoor stage.

1. The absence of a proscenium of any overhead structure eliminates the possibility of masking overhead lights. However, local lighting from behind proscenium pylons or screens is possible and generally should serve as an integral part of the lighting layout.

2. The use of towers set up at the back of the seating area as high as possible for the sake of angle of throw, can be used to house a number of arcs, projectors, or ellipsoidal spots with which to light the acting area. A central tower can be used for floodlighting; side towers for diagonal lighting of the acting areas, one from each side.

3. Footlights and background lights from trees or stands. Footlights can serve to mask changes in scenery by being turned toward the audience (bad practice) or used to illuminate a steam or water curtain.

4. Control. The centralized operating position generally consists of switching control only. Dimmers can be used for elaborate effects. There should be telephone and signal communication with director and various operators. Dimming and color changes may be made by means of opaque slides or remote boomerang control. The position of the control board should be such that effects can be seen easily.

PART TWO

APPLICATION

This is a reconsideration of the material of the first part in terms of a methodical application of lighting to the stage. Only when the student has a technical vocabulary and knows the tools with which he is to work, is he in a position to consider this procedure of application. The process of obtaining the preliminary knowledge should involve not only the working out of problems related to the material in each chapter, with the reading as suggested; but a certain amount of laboratory practice, use of instruments, and actual experience in the lighting of productions.

The organization of this Part is an attempt to put in the order of consideration the principles and methods which are involved in the design and use of light on the stage. The trial and error method, though existent to some degree in all productions, is unprofessional. A consideration of all the elements that enter the problem of lighting a production need not, as is often contended, kill feeling and inspiration. Inspiration which arises from a knowledge of all the variables and the possibilities can alone lead to results. In the theatre, where a number of separate techniques are involved and not the method of a single artist, this knowledge is more necessary than for a more individual expression.

The functions of light (mental images) comprise an artistic problem of relating visibility, naturalism, composition, and mood in the lighting of a particular scene; and the selection and use of equipment to perform these functions present a complicated technical problem. The four qualities of light (physiological stimuli) are present wherever light is used and they should be applied in varying aspects to objectify the functions already conceived. The various techniques and the procedure of application need to be outlined so that modern stage lighting has a more definite relation to the traditional methods of production.

Inasmuch as lighting in the theatre is designed to convince an audience without its being aware of it as lighting, per se, the process of application is much more in the nature of an art than a science. The designer can know the technical means of application, but in addition to these he must deal with the indefinite variables that are involved in any artistic expression. Lighting is not a simple means of expression nor can the judgment guaranteed to achieve artistic results be truly taught. It can, however, be cultivated through a knowledge of design and principles of application.

5. FUNCTIONS

The functions of lighting are a measure of its value to the stage. Our emotional, mental, and psychological reactions determine the degree of usefulness. The physiological characteristics of the eye are considered in the next chapter. The material here deals chiefly with mental reactions and the manner in which each quality of light influences them.

It is obviously unwise to try to make a rigid and inflexible delineation of psychological reactions, particularly in view of the complexity of sense stimuli and the influence of one sense upon another. However, for the sake of study, the following functions have been established as characteristic practical reactions to light and they may serve as objectives in any design of lighting. Any perception of light is accompanied by instinctive mental pictures, and the designer should attempt to evaluate the essential elements of each visual effect. The elements which influence mental reaction and the manner in which each quality of visual sense stimulation affects the final result are the items to consider in determining the extent of application of each function.

Light's most obvious function is to give visibility, but as all visual consciousness is gained through light it is possible to consider that the experience and associations gained in travel, the pleasure given by pictures, and the feeling of atmosphere obtained through the eyes and expressed in such terms as "homelike", "picturesque", "exotic", "peaceful", "stimulating", and so on, are also brought to consciousness chiefly through the visual process. In the development of the visual process, obviously influenced by the effects of light in nature, there is a tendency to identify any use of artificial light with naturalistic effects. Inasmuch as artificial light is man-made, there must be a certain selection involved in the determination of the distribution of light from artificial sources, and ultimately, just as nature gives a definite dramatic atmospheric quality in many of her lighting effects, so must the design of artificial lighting consider the atmosphere that can be produced.

I. VISIBILITY

When the range of visibility under natural light is considered and the same approach applied to the use of artificial light, it is obvious that, although the intensity of light is important, there are other qualities such as color, distribution, and movement which influence the creation of visibility that is desirable under different conditions. The visibility demanded for fine and detailed work is obviously different from that required for a general view of objects only. Generally the atmosphere surrounding objects in the field of vision contributes considerably to the individual's sense of visibility and very often objects seen not too clearly leave more to the imagination and thus take on a charm and dramatic quality which they do not possess ordinarily when seen distinctly. Good visibility is essentially selective. Its purpose is to reveal things selectively in terms of degrees of acuity.

II. NATURALISM

The time of day or season and the condition of the elements as expressed by the use of light on the stage are considered under this head. The problem of creating an illusion of naturalness by artificial means which are decidedly limited as to flexibility and complicated in number, requires a great deal of ingenuity and skill. The designer must be able to evaluate the essential elements of any naturalistic effect and select them for presentation in view of the technical means.

The realistic nature of the acting establishes the degree of naturalism which any picturization produced by artificial means should approach, but just as the actor represents a dramatic quality, the lighting should strive to create a selected and not a photographic effect. The abstract beauty of artificial effects of light and the facility with which they can be produced indicate that a direct decorative and pictorial effect can be produced easily. However, in order to make light serve with the actor in creating a subtle, convincing and unconscious visual effect, it should be designed to express a coordinated degree of naturalism.

Through the use of light it is possible to create the effect of some of the beauty of nature in the confined space of the stage. But the degree of illusion or its unconscious reception and its convincing reality depend upon careful design of the scenery in relation to the qualities of light and to its physical characteristics. Due to the necessity for the use of a number of instruments to create naturalistic effects, each area of the field of vision must be carefully illuminated and controlled in terms of qualities of light.

Much of the material in the previous section applies more definitely here. It is impossible to think of visibility under artificial light without referring to the standard of nature. Therefore, unless nature can be improved upon, we had better keep one eye on the actual and the other on the rather primitive tools we have with which to play God. It is infinitely easier to produce a spectacular display than a simple but convincing effect of sunset. In fact, let the student be as photographic, as naturalistic, in his approach as possible with the instruments and control means available, and even the best of them will produce a result so stylized that the untutored theatre-goer will have to stretch his imagination to recognize the intended effect. This is where the motion pictures excel. Anyone who can produce a convincing effect of naturalism in light on the stage can do anything else with it, because, in terms of the mechanical and arbitrary characteristics of the ordinary instrument, naturalism is most utterly stylized.

But the photographic effect is seldom dramatic. A random slice of nature set on the stage would generally be unsuccessful. In the concentration on naturalism, visibility—really the primary function of lighting—must not be forgotten. Motivation is the term applied to the effort to make visibility-lighting naturalistic. Sunlight, moonlight, daylight, lamplight, and firelight are naturalistic sources. When they can be produced convincingly and at the same time used to give the necessary visibility—say, on the acting area—then is the lighting of the scene motivated.

III. COMPOSITION

The selectivity in the distribution of light beyond photographic realism to promote ordered dramatic relationships is considered under this head. The proper use of the qualities that make light serve is an integral part of the production requires artistic judgment. The broad application of the term "style", which connotes selection, refers not only to the usual laws of harmony, form, and rhythm which stimulate the sensibilities pleasantly, but also to success in creating an appropriate dramatic picturization. It is an intellectual-aesthetic approach.

This special art of lighting in the theatre possesses certain phases of expression of all the visual arts and ties them together by means of movement to the vital quality of the actor. Through light, the beauty of architecture, sculpture, and painting as found in the setting can be lifted out of their static condition and made to live with the actor. In this respect, lighting becomes an art in itself. The medium has no lasting quality. It is essentially ephemeral, and therein lies its great charm. But our light sense is peculiarly undeveloped, so that we must rely upon the tests applied to the other arts.

The development of the electric lamp has made possible an extensive use of artificial light. Within the possibilities of control by electrical means and through a wide variety of light sources and instruments, it is possible to obtain a tremendous range of compositions in light, even to the approach of the dramatic quality of lighting found in nature. Yet these means have definite mechanical limitations. Knowing the part light plays in giving comfort and beauty under natural conditions and the tremendous function it serves in extending activities where natural light fails, compositions which are not possible to find in nature can be provided by artificial light.

IV. MOOD

The fundamental spirit of a play which the producer interprets for an audience through the medium of production is called mood. It depends directly upon the psychological reaction of the audience to the sense stimulations and the train of mental reactions which they set up.

In terms of light, the designer must sense the aims of the playwright, the methods of the producer, and the reactions of the audience to each particular phase in visual reaction. Next to the actor the greatest common denominator between the idea of the play and audience is light.

In describing the other functions of lighting it has been necessary to qualify each in terms of dramatic content. This aspect of visual experience by which light creates an atmosphere or an emotional response for an audience, is called mood. The motivation is identical with the fundamental conception of the playwright and is inferred in the lines or described in the manuscript.

The indefinite psychological reactions to various qualities of light, as they are influenced by experience, association, judgment, will, interest and abstract appeal, present a complicated problem which indicates that this function of light must wait on the future or more complete interpretation. For the present, let us consider how each quality of light affects the two simple emotions, comedy and tragedy. In general, extremes in any quality are associated with tragedy, the middle zone with comedy.

6. QUALITIES OF LIGHT

Every use of light, whether deliberately planned or not, affects the human being through his eyes in accordance with the characteristics of visual sensation. There are four properties of visual sensation, namely: intensity, color, form, and movement. Inasmuch as these are present in varying degrees wherever vision takes place, they should be designed to give a desired visual effect. They are essentially based upon the physiological reactions in the eye, the various details of which are considered in the study of Psychology. They are determining factors in any seeing experience and as such they constitute the physiological elements involved in any design of lighting.

If the eye is considered the apparatus which converts light radiation into nerve impulses for the mind to interpret, the light must be supplied to the eye in a recognizable intensity, color, distribution, and movement by external means. Instruments (the basic means as far as lighting is concerned) are designed to supply light radiation in terms of the qualities that the eye can use and it is for this reason that they are judged and used not so much for their efficiency, but because they can provide to a degree, these qualities.

I. INTENSITY OR BRIGHTNESS

The amount of radiation giving a range of vision between the limits of threshold-saturation stimulation is considered under intensity. From a physiological point of view it is supposedly determined by the sensitivity of the rods in the retina. This in turn is affected by the involuntary process of accommodation and adaptation of the retina, iris and lens of the eye. The range to which the eye is accustomed under natural light,—given in terms of illumination, roughly from .0001 to 13,000 foot-candles—permits great latitude in the design of artificial illumination.

Due to the characteristics of the eye (particularly the pupil adjustment and the retinal adaptation to contrasts) it is not necessary or practical, even if possible, to produce intensities by artificial means equal to the maximum amounts experienced in natural light. The eye accepts an appearance of brightness with a much lower intensity of radiation. Artificial light is never as general in its effect as natural light, so that contrasts enter into the consideration to such a degree, that fatigue due to saturation makes high intensities an actual liability.

The amount of light required to give a determinable sense of visibility depends upon the degree of acuity (distinctness) desired. Increases of intensity which cause stimulation, from absolute threshold where only generally masses can be seen, to the perception where fine detail becomes visible, must follow a logarithmic progression in order to give an arithmetic increase of distinctness of vision. Satisfactory illumination under favorable circumstances of light and shade and pigmentation have been tabulated in foot-candle tables for many different purposes. They are not absolute and should be used only as a starting figure. Excessive illumination not only causes fatigue due to saturation, but it is inefficient to the extent that the eye attempts to shut out the radiation if in excess of that which is necessary for the purpose at hand.

A. VISIBILITY

The amount of light necessary to give adequate visibility for different purposes in general is given in tables of foot-candles. This is influenced by the ability of objects to reflect or transmit the light falling on them. The product of the amount of illumination and the coefficient of reflection or transmission is called brightness.

Under natural illumination all things appear bright in proportion to their coefficients of reflection, but on the stage it is possible to determine the brightness by controlling the amount of illumination on certain objects or areas. Acting areas can be made brighter than scenery. As long as the audience is primarily interested in the actor, scenery should have only the amount of essential detail (a form of indication) which permits the imagination to complete the picture without distraction. Elaborate detail will not be seen if the amount of light falling on it is in proper proportion to that falling on the actors. Therefore, the elaboration is needless. Large expanses of cyclorama (stage sky), if bright, compete with the actor even though in nature we are forced to accept the really brilliant expanse of sky. So far there is no quantitative scale of brightness equal to the judgment of the eye. Experience as exhibited in the suggestions of the foot-candle tables for commercial lighting might very well extend to the stage. Motion picture camera men check their lighting with a brightness meter or test strips before shooting.

Perhaps some ambitious person will develop an accurate set of recommendations which will make clear the range of brightness desirable between the various parts of the stage and even the range of any part for various purposes or types of productions. Then the audience will never have to suffer the strain of trying to see through the dimness and gloom of "artistic" lighting nor the fatigue caused by too much brightness offered by the extreme apostles of the right.

B. NATURALISM

The relative effects on the stage may be at lower intensities than are usually found in nature. The brightness of the sky generally should be less than normal in order that the actor may stand out against it. Use motivating light on the acting area to justify its relatively increased intensity; low intensity on non-essential details.

C. COMPOSITION

The use of amounts of light selected from a pictorial and dramatic point of view to give appropriate composition in the bright-to-dark scale in each scene is the first consideration. Pictorially, light provides a far greater brightness range than painting, often as high as one to one thousand, where painting scarcely has a range greater than one to thirty. As a result great care must be taken to avoid glaring bright areas and dead, dark spaces. A broader standard of values must be acquired before any subtlety of expression can be demonstrated. A study of black-and-white photographs of some of the old masters in painting will serve as a starting point in the analysis of the relation of brightness values.

D. MOOD

There is a pleasure in brightly-lighted places consistent with comedy; the reverse is true for tragedy.

II. COLOR

Color, or the quality of light, has been very little considered in comparison with its use in the fields of painting and decoration. The possibilities of creating color effects in terms of light are greatly extended beyond the usual consideration of color in terms of pigment seen under natural light, and are complicated by contrasts and the temporal nature of light. The appearance of pigment depends upon the color of the illuminating light.

The cones of the retina supposedly react to a certain range of wave lengths without analyzation, not only in the particular zone of wave lengths, called hue, but to the degree of purity,—that is, the relative lack of admixture with other visible wave lengths, called saturation, and perhaps in conjunction with the rods, to the amount of stimulation called brightness. Thus, there are three distinguishable dimensions of color.

The eye always accepts the composite result of wave lengths of a certain brightness as a color reaction and does not break it up into its component parts. This adaptability to the reception of a composite result is accompanied by reactions which tend to emphasize contrasts in hue, saturation and brightness. In the final analysis, color is light and in order to be able to determine the effect, the elements which influence its production and the characteristics of reception should be taken into consideration.

Perhaps due to the ability of the lens to focus more distinctly the wave lengths of the central zone of the spectrum, the eye is more sensitive under normal intensity to yellow-green than it is to red and violet. Blues and violets of high saturation cause fatigue quickly if the brightness is high. Tints of color approaching white light give the best degree of visibility. A balance of hues gives the general effect of white.

The light tone solid, a three-dimensional graph of the distinguishable shades and tints, is a useful means for studying color combinations in terms of the 3-color process, and it supplies a physiological definition of color tone.

A. VISIBILITY

The sensitivity or luminosity curve shows that the eye sees more clearly under colors in the yellow-green zone of the spectrum than under the end zones, red and blue. Likewise tints of color convey a greater sense of acuity than those which are pure, even where the latter are of equal or greater brightness.

It is strange to note that any fair degree of brightness of artificial light seems to cause fatigue more quickly than ordinary natural illumination. Many customers object to the 100-foot-candles of illumination in a New York store when they come in off the street where the illumination is often over 100 times this amount. This is due in a large measure to surprise, but beyond this, and probably included in it, is the fact that the color is different from natural light.

Try reading a newspaper under a neon light; or sometime in the theatre after you have joined the audience in applauding a brilliant, rich, Maxfield Parrish blue sky when the curtain goes up, stop to analyse why every actor seems to have a halo silhouette and why your eyes begin to ache if the scene is too long—too much contrast, too strong a blue

B. NATURALISM

The subtle shades and tints of color found in nature, as the painter uses pigment, are good examples to follow; warm color in strong directed light for sunlight; cool color to illuminate the shadows for daylight.

C. COMPOSITION

Most theories on the use of color are concerned primarily with pigment as it appears under a standard of white light. The range of color in light does not provide greater choice than that possible in pigment painting, but tints and shades as a product of brightness variation increase this range proportionately. The resultant effect of colored light on pigment complicates the approach from the standpoint of tone relations in painting, but, by an allowance for the effect of light on pigment, the painters' methods serve as a starting point for creating good composition with color in light.

D. MOOD

Warm colors are associated with comedy, cool with tragedy, but aesthetic and symbolic interpretations of color alter this to a degree. Tints of color go with comedy, pure strong colors with tragedy.

III. FORM

The retina being composed of a mosaic of end fibres registers sensation as a photographic plate in two dimensions, not only as a pattern of black and white, but in definite colors. Only within one or two degrees does what we call distinct vision take place. The sense of form in space beyond the distance where accommodation and convergence operate is obtained by experience, and within that distance the relation of objects in space and their solidity or form is established by stereoscopic vision. Likewise, the muscular action accompanying the shifting of the eyes to include details in the angle of sharp vision delineates the size, shape and position of objects, as well as the various details of surface form. The eye is invariably attracted to the brightest object or area in the field of vision. By means of controlling the distribution of light and creating patterns and compositions of light and shade, it is possible to produce sensations on the retina that will be interpreted as forms in space.

The simultaneous contrasts of color and intensity in patterns are enforced and the effect of each is different when observed singly.

With a comfortable balance of light and shade, a distinctness of form and detail is provided by less illumination (from the standpoint of visibility) than is given by natural light.

Through a knowledge of the signs of space perception, it is possible to reproduce large spaces in small areas and to diminish the appearance of large spaces. 1. Lines of perspective, 2. Sharpness and clearness of outline, 3. Superposition, 4. Position of shadows and shading, 5. Relative motion, 6. Relative color, and 7. Scale.

A. VISIBILITY

The direct rays of sunlight and even moonlight have educated us to depend on the contrasts of light and shade to see the solidity of form of objects. Even on a gray day, when the solidity or plastic nature of the surface of an object is minimized by the absence of high light, shade, and shadow, the pattern of shapes is conveyed to the eye by contrasts of brightness and color. The contrasts in nature are not under control as they are on the stage, so that we are able to provide even greater acuity with artificial light.

Contrasts also have their extremes which cause fatigue and limit visibility accordingly. Nature is a good guide but does not go far enough. Objects are seen most distinctly and naturally when the rays of the sun are coming from behind the observer over his left or right shoulder along a 45° angle both in plan and elevation. This gives a normal balance between light and shade and shadow is illuminated softly by general distribution from the sky.

Where there is no contrast, there is no sense of form, for example: a white ball in front of a white surface illuminated evenly from all directions (general lighting) disappears completely in the background. Change the color of the ball of the background or "gray" either, and the ball appears as a round silhouette shape, a flat disc. Only as the lighting becomes directional does the spherical shape appear. It will be seen that diagonal lighting from one direction and the inclusion of the cast shadow indicate the shape and position best.

Sharp contrasts beyond the normal range tend to exaggerate form. The glowing portion of the half or quarter moon looks much larger than the unlighted portion of the disc shows it to be. We even have to be told that it is a sphere. We don't often look at the sun, our daytime light source, but at night we are faced with a myriad of irritating points stabbing our eyes and we blindly accept the torment for the benefit of the feeble illumination given.

The eye automatically focuses on the brightest object in the field of vision and other objects become correspondingly less visible.

B. NATURALISM

Imitate the essential details of relative intensity and color in naturalistic distribution—sunset, sunrise, moonlight. Associated detail and the use of signs of space perception lend conviction most directly. A combination of strong direct light and low general light give naturalistic high lights and shadows and are natural to spotlighting, but the subtleties of reflected light and the soft diffusion of daylight are difficult to produce even with the best border and footlights.

C. COMPOSITION

The form of the plastic pictorial effect on the stage is the most important aspect of composition. Form includes the distribution of light in connection with the sculptural, architectural design of surfaces of solid objects, creating a visual pattern of light and shade and color in the eye. Here again, the aesthetic principles of the relationship of forms, in position, measure, and shape which have been developed upon the hypothesis of the fixed conditions of natural light can only serve as a starting point.

With artificial illumination, the range of expression is considerably increased by the control over light distribution. The location of the source, the power of the instrument, and the direction of the rays determine the position and the size of the shadow of an object, and its brightness and degree of emphasis in the composition. The graded effect of tone on large areas is a natural characteristic of strip lighting. The description of the ball under visibility indicated how, by controlling the distribution of light, forms can be exaggerated or suppressed. A general flood of color acts like a unifying wash laid over a painting. With dimmers it is possible to balance the distribution or brightness and color from each source so that they fit within the composition.

Again let the student consult the old masters. Men like Leonardo da Vinci and Rembrandt were very conscious of light. What would they do with artificial light as we can control it today?

90

D. MOOD

Detail and balanced contrasts are associated with comedy.   Large masses and sharp contrasts or no contrast go with tragedy.

IV. MOVEMENT

Any change in intensity, color or form of light is considered under movement. It is the quality that gives life to visual sensation. Considering the effects of light on the stage and the beautiful compositions demonstrated by Wilfred's Clavilaux, we have the range of possibilities of expression to light that is common to all the fine arts. We can add the rhythm and dramatic qualities of music and poetry to architecture, sculpture, and painting.

The eye, just as does any other sensory organ, requires a certain amount of time to be stimulated so that sensations can be reorganized into nerve impulses for transmission to the mind. The time required, and that used, depend upon a number of variables, such as desire for visibility and study, expected sequences, acquaintance with the subject, and so on. Motion pictures which present more than sixteen sets of stimulation (flashes of individual pictures) every second give a sense of continuous movement. Unexpected sequences or abstract variations cause fatigue if changed too rapidly. Switching lights on and off or moving too quickly from one distribution to another is apt to be a shock to the eye. Likewise, the rapid shifting of the eye to take in shapes of large objects or to see as much in the field of vision as possible, links form and movement in an inseparable bond.

Movement of the actors on the stage in an otherwise static lighting generally offers the only change of pattern on the retina. It is impossible to follow musical beats with changes in light unless these changes are subtle, or recognizable in form and somewhat expected. Subtle changes in intensity, color, and form are in keeping with light in nature, but can generally be faster as long as they are smooth. In this way it is possible to make light live, and change the appearance of things around us. If carefully done, in view of the above, these changes can be really dramatic. Movement in the field of vision always attracts attention.

Changes in intensity, color and form, if expected, can be rapid. Fatigue is caused by rapid and unexpected change. Time for analyzation of detail on important objects should be allowed. The simulation of effects in nature should be slow and imperceptible. There is a dramatic quality in an imperceptible change in lighting.

A. VISIBILITY

Nature has educated us to accept an infinite variety. Once we see and become acquainted with an object or person only the essential details need be present for memory to complete the picture. Even a painting does not seem to change from one time of day to another, as long as there is sufficient light to see it at all.

The changes in natural light are generally slow but constant. When clouds rush by bringing sudden darkness and lightning flashes, we cannot help but be moved. The eye is slow in adjusting to changes also and it is only after some exposure to a scene that we feel acquainted with the details—that it is visible. Visibility takes time and flashes or momentary glimpses cause fatigue. On the other hand, many an office worker suffers eye strain when working under artificial light, probably largely because there is no change to rest the eyes.

B. NATURALISM

One should study the use of the complete gamut of distinguishable brightness, colors, and distribution as we know them in nature; for example, the changing effects of sunset. Subtle or immediate changes in all the qualities are in order where nature has them, but remember that most sunrises on the stage are not at Mandalay with "China 'cross the bay".

C. COMPOSITION

The theories and practice of harmony, counterpoint and rhythm of musical composition can serve as a guide for interpreting visual changes in the foregoing qualities of light for the eye, as music does for the ear. With immobile scenery, even with static lighting the actors move from one grouping to another, thereby changing the composition. But more obviously, any alteration in the distribution, color, or intensity of lighting changes the picturization.

D. MOOD

Reasonably rapid changes in any of the above qualities convey comedy. Tragedy is either of staccato tempo or slow and ponderous in movement. Bringing up the lights on a scene gives pleasure and excitement. Lowering the illumination creates suspense, peace or depression. Changes in color and form tend to swing the emotion to an opposite condition.

7. TECHNICAL ELEMENTS

This chapter deals with the means for making practical the various plans which have been designed in relation to the characteristic mental and physiological reactions of the observer. It is a form of check list covering all the technical aspects to be considered in carrying out any lighting problem. The details of each part have been described in the chapters on apparatus. The means of producing artificial lighting involve a technical problem dealing with the light source, the instrument, distribution and the object lighted. The available equipment, methods of use, and the design of the objects to be illuminated determine the technique of application of light to each problem.

All the elements must be designed in complete relation to one another, and they should allow for as extensive an expression of the four qualities of light as is consistent with the purposes for which it is to be used. This coordination is absolutely essential. The laws of physics, dealing with transmission, reflection, refraction, and color of light are the bases of the design of these elements. They are used in relation to the laws of electricity, the characteristics of tungsten lamps, and the methods of wiring and control. A thorough knowledge of these relationships can only be gained through experience in the actual handling of equipment. The use of available light sources, and instruments for modeling light, and an understanding use of their distribution, are the practical methods whereby the production of the resultant distribution can be created most effectively in relation to the objects to be illuminated. The variables involved in this process are so complicated that only by understanding the detailed characteristics of each, can a planned effect be produced.

I. THE LIGHT SOURCE

The adjustment of our eyes and the conduct of our whole lives in relation to the effects of light from a single light source—the sun—determine a standard which should serve as a guide in the use of artificial light. Obviously no artificial source can provide the conditions supplied by the sun. But with the sources available, the disadvantage is offset somewhat by the entension of absolute control over them. The extent to which the various qualities can be produced and controlled through artificial light sources is the foundation upon which the structure of technique is built.

A. BRIGHTNESS

The brightness of the light source involves:

1. Candle-power intensity in all directions.

2. Total output expressed in lumens.

3. The unit-area brightness of the filament or light source, expressed in lamberts or candles-per-square-inch.

4. Efficiency expressed in lumens-per-watt.

5. The available wattages in stock types of light sources.

6. Voltage at lamp.

B. COLOR

The color of the light source is concerned with:

1. The analysis of its characteristic radiation in terms of the various wave lengths created. Illustrated by a color cutoff.

2. The different color cutoffs of various types of lamps. The spectral characteristics of the incandescent filament at varying degrees of temperature.

3. Available colored sources. Gaseous and vapor tubes, arcs, natural color and dipped or sprayed lamps. Fluorescent colors.

C. DISTRIBUTION

The form of distribution deals with:

1. A point source of light and spherical emanation.

2. The analysis of densities of light rays proceeding out into space along straight lines in all directions from an irregular light source. The units of density of light rays in certain directions expressed in candle-power distribution and made graphic by distribution curves.

3. The characteristics of tungsten filament as to length, cross section, and burning brightness.

4. Shapes and sizes of filaments or light sources, the shapes of bulbs, sizes, and construction. Quartzline, Xenon, and arc sources.

5. Reflector lamps: Spotlight, flood, silver bowl, and side-silvered tubular lamp.

D. CONTROL

The variation of the qualities of light in the source is provided by:

1. Candle-power variation effected by changes in voltage or current through dimmers. Capacities, sizes, and characteristics of operation of dimmers. Slight time lag in tube-reactor and motor control.

2. Color variation in the filament in type B and C. Yellowish white at full intensity to reddish tinge at low brightness. Future development of a radiator which will create any wave length desirable.

3. Distribution changes due to intensity and color variation.

4. Instantaneous heating of the filament. Immediate control by switching. Slow changes at low dimmer reading. Number of steps required. Fechner's law and dimmer characteristics.

II. THE INSTRUMENT

Instruments are in a sense accessories to the light source and are generally designed to shape or model the rays of direct emanation. In the chapter on instruments, the manner in which the instruments provide a range of control over the various qualities of light through various physical laws has been covered more or less in detail. Their selection to provide a special type of distribution, in view of the position, in relation to the object lighted and the observer, depends upon the combined effects of all the instruments used and the extent of control which can be had over them.

A. INTENSITY

Intensity is expressed in terms of beam-candle-power and is chiefly determined by the wattage of the light source.

The output is influenced by:

1. The efficiency of the instrument, determined in percentage: the output of the instrument divided by the total lumens given out by the light source. Accessories further affecting efficiency:

    a. The amount of reflection due to material, color, and surface used in the reflector. The amount of light gathered and the size and shape of the reflector in relation to the dimensions and position of the light source.

    b. The amount of transmission of glass, gelatin, etc., due to the material, thickness, shape, and color in the lens, diffuser, or color medium.

    c. The amount of absorption or loss of light due to inefficiency in relation or transmission and the absorption characteristics of the inside of the hood and cutoffs of all kinds.

2. Operating Efficiency. Determined by the position of the filament in relation to reflectors, lenses, and absorbing mediums. Inefficiency results from: using too little of the total emanation from the source, sources not sufficiently concentrated, off the optical center with the wrong focal length, off the axis, and where the rays are subject to spherical and chromatic aberration.

3. Maintenance affects efficiency in accordance with:

    a. Life of the lamp and replacement.

    b. Durability of reflecting surfaces and transmission mediums.

    c. Cleanliness.

4. Watts Required. The selection of wattage for intensity is determined by the lumen output of the instrument for various distances of throw in relation to the coefficient of transmission of the color medium and coefficients of absorption of the accessories, such as cutoffs, etc.

B. COLOR

The range of color from an instrument expressed in hue, saturation, and brightness deals with:

1. Light tone solid for single light source units and for three and four color circuits.

2. The subtractive effect of the color cutoff of the light source combined with the selective transmission or reflection of the mediums used to color the light, included in the instrument.

3. The subtractive system. The selection of secondary colors for color magazines and boomerangs. The degree of mixing.

4. Types of color mediums. Gelatin, glass, cinemoid, etc. Ultra-violet and infrared filters. The specifications for color mediums are: Purity. Permanence. Transmission. Nonhydroscopic. Mechanical strength. Variety. Flame-proof. Cost.

C. FORM OF DISTRIBUTION

The distribution of light from each instrument is its distinguishing characteristic and the gage of the density of light rays in all directions from it. The details concerned are:

1. Lumen output measured by a candle-power distribution curve.

2. The shape of light distribution expressed by the solid form of the distribution curve, generally symmetrical about an axis in the case of spots and floods, but slightly irregular due to the shape and dimensions of the filament. Asymmetrical from strip lights and special instruments.

3. The optical means of controlling and modelling the rays of natural emanation from the light source through the laws of reflection, refraction, and absorption. Reflectors, lenses, cutoffs. (Refer to the chapter on instruments.)

    a. Reflectors. Spherical, parabolic, ellipsoidal, and irregular. Giving regular, spread, diffuse, or specular reflection; of a material which stands up under heat; of a practical size to gather most effectively the greatest amount of emanation in relation to the light source; of a shape to reflect the rays in the proper direction; of a position in relation to the light source which considers the construction and dimensions of the filament; and of a color which gives the greatest range.

    b. Refracting Mediums. Lenses of a size, focal length and shape to gather the rays of light most effectively. A certain amount of light is lost in passing through lenses due to reflection and absorption, but they provide the most definite means for controlling rays and projected images. Diffusing mediums in the form of frosted gelatin, or hammered, frosted, or prismatic glass, give degrees of diffusion and multiple direction to the rays.

    c. Absorbing Mediums or Cutoffs. Used for the elimination of rays not emanating in a useful direction. Louvers, fins, mats, and so on.

    d. Patterns of light by means of slides.

4. Types of instruments are determined chiefly by their distribution curves and are considered in four groups:

    a. Spotlights. Concentrated beam, single light source, giving a high intensity and a definite direction, under good control, but of relatively low- to medium-lumen, output efficiency. Plano-convex lens spots, fresnel spots, and ellipsoidal reflector spots.

    b. Floodlights. Flood beam from single light source or a number of closely-grouped small sources as in a bunch light, giving a broad spread of relatively low intensity, moderate control, and relatively high efficiency, or a narrow high intensity beam given by projectors.

    c. Strip Lights. General distribution from many sources mounted in a row, giving shadowless general distribution of low intensity, little control, and relatively high efficiency. Several strips mounted one above the other constitute a bank which gives even more diffusion.

    d. Special Instruments. Those giving definite patterns of light by projection or other means, a moderate intensity, definite control, and relatively low efficiency, and all instruments used purely for decorative or motivating effect, such as wall brackets and chandeliers, fireplaces, and so on.

D. CONTROL

Control of light changes at the instrument consists in the following items.

1. Full intensity of the light source to "out," by dimming.

2. Color changes due to intensity variation in different lamps in the same unit, by changes in color medium, by boomerang or magazine under remote control, or by hand at the instrument.

3. Distribution changes controlled by dimming, focusing, changing direction, transmission mediums, or reflectors. Use of cutoffs: iris.

4. Structural conditions involved in mounting instruments in the space required for flexibility in use, and the subtle manipulation of control at the switchboard.

III. DISTRIBUTION

The resulting form of the density, color, and direction of light rays in space from all the instruments of various types that are used to achieve a desired effect is considered under the heading of distribution. Until light is brought into a space, the existence of objects can only be known through feeling, hearing, or smelling. By all odds the greatest contact with the outside world is due to the existence of light rays in the space in which objects exist.

In order to distinguish objects in a natural or specially selected manner so that the proper visibility and atmosphere are given, a definite distribution of light must be provided. The methods of using instruments to create lighting effects in order to make light serve its various functions, particularly for obtaining naturalistic effects, are determined by the instruments, and the special demands of production. As a result, light is distributed from special groups of instruments over the acting area, the setting, the background (such as cyclorama or backdrop), and special features that vary from one production to another. These methods involve particularly the direction and the position of instruments and their ability to send light rays out into space, in order to illuminate the object properly from the standpoint of the observer.

The inability of one instrument to give a range of the qualities of light requires the use of several sources. Intensity is determined by the candle power and the number of instruments directed on a point. Color range is dependent upon changing color mediums or the use of three light sources in the same position. General form depends upon the regulation of the distribution from all the instruments.

A. INTENSITY

The illumination of objects in space by several instruments is determined by the additive effect of all the rays that are superimposed at any point on the object lighted, and considers:

1. The amount of visual radiation falling on a point in space determined by the additive result of all the rays passing through this point directly from the light sources and by reflection from or transmission through surrounding objects. It involves:

    a. The amount at each point on a plane designated by the illumination curve.

    b. The foot-candle value at a point determined by the density of the light flux in candle-power divided by the distance squared. The inverse square law.

    c. Amount of illumination from several instruments (an enlarged source acts as several instruments) figured by the additive result of all their distributions on the point.

2. The required illumination is determined by a specified brightness. Brightness is the result of the illumination in foot candles times the coefficient of reflection of the object lighted and is measured in terms of foot-lamberts. Tables.

3. Computation. Computation of the illumination on the acting area, which is lighted directly by spotlights and blended by X-rays and not dependent particularly upon illumination by reflection from surrounding objects, can be figured directly by the distribution curve of each spotlight illuminating it, considering the color used and the spread of focus. The computation of illumination from the X-rays and the footlights can be figured by the point

to point method, although the extreme complexity of additive distributions from these sources is too great to make this method practical. Inasmuch as these often contribute less than ten percent to the illumination, they need not be considered. Computations for stage lighting can serve only as a check to determine the adequate amount of illumination and should not be followed too rigidly. Inasmuch as the final effect of illumination is almost impossible to predetermine, it can only be achieved experimentally by the regulation of intensity in each unit.

    a.   Figure the additive effect on each acting area from the distribution curve of the spotlights used in relation to the colors.

    b.   The complication of calculating the additive effect of lighting units where a number of light sources are concerned and their general positions in relation to the object lighted are established, made necessary a simpler system of figuring intensity called the flux of light method. See Illuminating Engineering handbooks.

B. COLOR

Color, like illumination, is the result of the additive effect of the various wave lengths and intensities of light passing through a point in space. Obviously, no two points will have exactly the same color composition unless the illumination is evenly distributed between them. The items involved are:

1.   The creation of color with light at a point in space caused by additive effect of all wave lengths passing through that point and the resultant shade or tint only being distinguished in composite form by the eye.

2.   Use of the three- or four-color system based on light-tone-solid possibilities.

3.   The selection of color mediums to produce a balance of white or proper tonality on a point. From the standpoint of pigment, the subtractive effect of selective reflection. For surfaces in relation to form, consideration of the direction and wave length of the rays from each light source.

4.   Psychological effect, and adaptation to dominant tone.

C. FORM

It is usually necessary to use several types of instruments to produce the desired lighting effects. The direction of light from each instrument, the position that is established thereby in relation to the object lighted, and the composite result of the distributions from each instrument produce the form of illumination in space. This is the cause of the development of methods and equipment discussed in previous chapters. Form is determined by:

1.   Direction. Determined by the reflection or transmission of light rays from objects to the eye. The direction of the rays of light illuminating objects should be determined from the standpoint of the functions of light, i.e., the use of naturalistic directions as determined by light from the sun, the sky, and objects about us and the compositional arrangement of high lights and shadows.

    a.   High light and shadow are due to a straight-line transmission. The space behind objects and in the direction of the rays receives no light and is called shadow. The surface of the object not in direct line with the rays is called shade. The area on which the shadow falls is called cast shadow. High light, light, shade, and shadow give plasticity to solid form. Position of shadow important. The illumination of the shadow by general light of a complimentary color. The position of cast shadow establishes the position of the object in space. Complicated shadows from multiple units destroy the sense of plasticity and naturalness. A soft edge to shadows given by large sources are less distracting.

b. Light rays should be directed only on the areas to be illuminated. The problem of confining light to a definite shape, particularly where only a small area is to be illuminated and the surrounding space is to be unseen, presents almost an impossible problem for solution. Spill or stray light from the instrument, particularly where soft edge is desired, and diffuse reflected light from the object lighted are almost impossible to eliminate, so that objects with a high reflecting coefficient—white or polished—are apt to be visible even though they are out of the direct line of distribution from the light source.

2. <u>Position.</u> Established by the direction desired in relation to the structural features of the building and setting, and their relation to the audience. The demand for flexibility of direction indicates that there should be great flexibility of position for various types of instruments. Practical features discussed in the chapter on equipment indicate the extent of flexibility desirable so that the various types of instruments can be fed from a number of positions. Position is determined by the following items:

a. The form of distribution desired determines the types of instruments that should be used, in view of their practical limitations.

b. The distance of throw and color medium used generally determine the candle-power necessary and may require the use of an arc or several incandescent units from one position.

c. Generally all lighting instruments except those which illuminate the auditorium should be masked in order to be least distracting.

d. Light must fill the space in which objects are apt to move. Generally speaking, it is always practical, particularly in relation to the arbitrary use of light, to have the light source as close to the object lighted as is possible.

3. <u>Balance.</u> The composite distribution of several instruments using different colors. In view of the direction and position of the various instruments, and the characteristic distribution from each, the color used and the slight effect of reflection from the floor cloth, scenery, and costumes, the final effect can only be obtained experimentally by regulating the intensities from each unit to obtain balanced color and balanced form. The proper composition of light distribution thus can only be obtained by providing adequate intensity in the various instruments and a means for controlling it. However, sufficient flexibility in the original plans should be allowed to obtain this balance.

4. <u>Traditional Practice.</u> Direction is determined by the possible positions for mounting instruments. Too often the traditional positions determine an arbitrary direction which defeats any sense of subtlety. Flexibility of direction for projecting light rays has a precedent in the numerous cross reflections from objects under natural light; and in the theatre, where intensities are much lower than under natural conditions, consideration of direction should be for effect and not confined to the directions established by the traditional positions for instruments. Lighting layouts for shows.

D. VARIETY OR CHANGE

The control of the distribution of light in space so that it has the qualities that give proper visual stimulation requires the use of various types of instruments to project light in color and intensity only where desired. Where movement is concerned, the instruments must be selected in view of the range of distribution of intensity, color, and form that they can give. Control considers:

1. Movement in relation to static objects dependent upon the change in their illumination.

a. Intensity variation by dimmers. Capacity and grouping to allow for control over various instruments.

b. Changes in color by dimming or boomerang control. Changes in color of light through the whole spectrum generally possible only with three-color strips.

c. Changes in form by follow spots, but generally dependent upon varying intensity and color from the different instruments in fixed positions.

2. Changes in distribution to simulate naturalistic effects.

3. Control of distribution to give a range of intensity, color, and form in various compositions, giving a rhythm of change consistent with the dramatic nature of a play by automatic control by the operator or artist at the console.

4. Changes to produce arbitrary dramatic effects or the constant change to follow every dramatic situation in creating a definite mood. The arbitrary use of the curtain and the division of the play into various scenes influenced by technical limitations of equipment.

IV. THE OBJECT LIGHTED

The general term "object" is applied to things which are not self-luminous, but which are seen because of the light reflected from them to the eye. Inasmuch as most of the things that we see are not self-luminous, their appearance depends upon the intensity, color, form, and movement of the illuminating light. From the standpoint of the object itself, its pigment, texture, shape, size, and position, which are usually fixed (though not always), are determining factors in its appearance under the illumination that is provided. From the standpoint in which it is seen by the observer, the relation of the object to the direction of the light rays determines the angle of reflection to the eye. The angle of vision which brings only certain details into sharp delineation must be considered. Although the object in this chapter suggests individual subjects, the relation between all objects in the field of vision determines the composition and should be considered from the standpoint of design.

The appearance of objects under natural light is the accepted condition for pictorial design, so that when their appearance under artificial light is being considered, the same subjective standards of taste apply. The difference between the two, however, demands an entirely new approach to the use of the pigment, form, and texture of objects in order to achieve results in artificial illumination comparable to design under natural light. Beyond this, there are many possibilities, such as changing the appearance of objects by means of artificial light, which cannot be achieved under natural conditions. Design under artificial light can achieve dramatic effects which are not within the realm of expression under daylight conditions, because the intimate relation between the object lighted and the illuminating means, is under control.

The following outline considers the details of objects in terms of the qualities of light. As secondary light sources, which they are when they reflect or transmit light to the eye, objects are as important in creating a visual effect as the illuminating means.

A. BRIGHTNESS

The ability of objects to transmit or reflect light to the eye under normal conditions is a constant characteristic of the object. Variation in the illuminating light is the only means of changing the effect of its appearance. Brightness is the product of the illumination, times the coefficient of reflection or transmission. Foot-lamberts.

The distance from the object lighted to the eye does not enter the consideration to any extent. Inasmuch as most objects have diffusing surfaces, the angle of the cone of light rays directed to the eye by the area lighted (only the rays sent to the eye make the object visible) varies according to the distance the observer is from the object lighted. It varies also accordingly, to the change in the area stimulated on the retina due to this angle, and compensates in both cases for the increased distance between the object lighted and the observer. The object appears approximately as "bright" no matter what the distance to the observer may be.

1. The coefficient of reflection, "value" in pigment terms. The proportion of light reflected

regardless of the amount of illumination. Inversely it is the measure of the absorption that takes place, due to pigmentation. Equal steps from white through gray to black are logarithmic. The coefficients that appear as equal steps to the eye, in ten steps, roughly, are 90, 66, 48, 35, 25, 16, 9.5, 5, 2.6, 1.4 percents.

    a. White or light surfaces tend to pick up any stray light; and, where lighting is to be confined to certain areas, the coefficient of reflection of surrounding objects should be low.

    b. A light setting which has a higher coefficient of reflection than the actor's face is always more apt to distract than one painted a lower value.

    c. The effect of a white-plastered wall can be obtained by using grays, a procedure which allows for much more freedom in the distribution of light.

2. The amount of illumination required in view of the coefficient of reflection for various purposes. The amount of illumination helps to determine the brightness of pigment combinations. Decreasing illumination can give any degree of value to a perfectly white surface. Likewise, a complementary color in light lowers the brightness of a pigment. A similarly-colored light tends to increase the effect of brightness.

3. Brightness due to position and type of reflecting surface in relation to light source and observer. Cosine law of emission. Specular reflection.

4. Contrasts. The differences in the effect of brightness due to contrast or lack of contrast. Surfaces seen against dark surroundings always seem more bright than when seen alone or against equally bright backgrounds. On a plane surface, the brightest part is that which appears adjacent to a darker background and vice versa.

5. Brightness of transmission compared to reflection. Translucent backdrops and shades over fixtures always appear brighter with less light expended than surfaces which reflect light to the eye, chiefly because of darker backgrounds.

B. PIGMENT CHARACTERISTICS

Pigment is only one of the elements used to determine the color effect that reaches the eye. It is a chemical which has the ability to reflect certain wave lengths and to absorb others. The knowledge of the appearance of pigments is based primarily upon their effect under daylight conditions and their mixture is always subtractive. The details to consider in relation to lighting are:

1. Tone relations in value, intensity and color. The preponderance of visual compositions are designed in terms of pigment combinations. Subtleties of tints and shades. Harmony, sequence, and balance of tone relations.

2. The selective reflection that pigment offers to various wave lengths of light. Analyzed by the spectral cutoff and defined in terms of brightness, hue and saturation, in terms of the three primary colors or the coefficient of reflection to red, green, and blue light.

3. The resultant effect of colored light on pigment in terms of hue, saturation, and brightness, determined by the common transmission or reflecting elements between the two cutoffs. Illuminating light must contain wave lengths which can be reflected by the pigment in order for an effect to be seen. Conversely, if the pigment color is to be reduced in brightness, or its normal effect is to be changed, the illuminating color must be short of those wave lengths.

4. Systems of painting for variety of effect under colored light. Neutral backgrounds or stippled secondaries. Selection of pigment in relation to the color of the motivating light to be used.

5. Photoluminescent chemicals. Dye, makeup and paint. Fluorescent and phosphorescent colors. Best seen with little or no other light present.

C. FORM OF THE OBJECT LIGHTED

Aside from the coefficient of reflection and its pigment color, the texture of the surface and its shape, size, and position are important determining factors in the appearance of the object lighted. The details to consider are:

1. Surface texture determining the kind of reflection—regular, spread, diffuse, or specular. Rough surface always more diffuse. Excess illumination tends to give specular reflection.

2. Size, shape, and position of the surface determining the pattern of light on the retina.

   a. Size. The outline of an object or the various details of its surface are usually distinguished by the eye as two-dimensional images. If its relation to known objects is established and the object and its background have different coefficients of reflection of color, the size of the object can be definitely established. If these are not present, the size becomes only vaguely apparent.

   b. Shape. The sense of shape depends upon the boundary or silhouette extent of stimulation as indicated by the differences in coefficient of reflection, of color, texture, and the angle of adjacent planes and can be emphasized or suppressed in these terms as they produce a pattern on the retina. Shape is most easily distinguished by the differences caused by light and shade.

   c. Position. Determined by relation to other objects in space. Cosine law of emission determines its brightness in relation to the direction of the light. Signs of space perception. Stereoscopic vision.

3. High light, shade, shadow, and reflected tone give a sense of third dimension. Direction of light in relation to the object lighted. Complication of direction from various instruments.

4. Secondary sources. Ceiling, walls, transparent and translucent screens, floor cloth, costumes and make-up.

5. The form of the setting. Aside from being arranged to satisfy certain production requirements, such as sight lines, entrances and exits, furniture, etc., provision should be made in the design of the setting for projecting light into the acting area, as from the teaser and tormentors; through openings for motivating sunlight, daylight or moonlight, by the use of fixtures in positions that suggest motivation of the necessary illumination; and on backgrounds consisting of cycloramas, ground rows, etc. Arranged so that they can be lighted most effectively by the available instruments. Use of masking pieces, hollow columns, juts in the scenery, and screens, to hide special instruments. Allowance for the effective use of gauzes, translucencies, and cycloramas.

6. Dramatic or compositional emphasis. The suppression or exaggeration of detail and form. Use of solid scenery adjacent to actor, or where cast shadows are desired. Painted perspective, and moldings in the background where the illumination is low, or where solid form cannot be compared easily.

7. Use of scale models. Valuable for studying the general distribution and arrangement of the set and its color in relation to the available lighting. Also useful to study light changes that cannot be indicated in a sketch.

D. VARIETY IN THE OBJECT LIGHTED

The fixed condition of most objects aside from the actor calls for the use of changing light to vary their appearance. Settings to be seen under different distributions of light must be designed in consideration of the lighting. The elements to consider are:

1. Coefficient of reflection determining the degree of change of intensity due to the effect of illumination from any one instrument. The position of the object in relation to the direction of rays from another light source may change its effect of brightness, but the general effect is due to the dimming on and off of the light from the various instruments.

2. Change of pigment effect depending upon the change in the color of the illuminating light. Use of neutral or spattered backgrounds for variety of effect.

3. Change of form of the setting aside from actually moving the setting itself, depending upon changes in the distribution of lighting. The movement of the actor about the stage constantly changes the effect in an otherwise static distribution of light. Moving scenery, such as panoramas, shifting gauzes, smoke, or the actual movement of parts of the scene can be effective providing movement is not distracting. The convention of raising the curtain. Use of the revolving stage and elevators in movement during a scene.

4. The dramatic quality of change of effect aside from the movement of the actor, depending primarily upon smoothness of control of the distribution of light. Shifting emphasis to suit the change in the mood of the play.

8. PROCEDURE

Up to this point the discussion has dealt with lighting as a problem in itself. Its use as an integral part of production depends upon its relation to all the elements that enter the process of presenting the idea of the playwright to an audience through the medium of the theatre. The coordination involves a certain procedure which considers this relationship for various types of plays and styles of production. Traditionally the methods of procedure which are vaguely known as professional practice, or production principles, have slowly been influenced by each new development that serves as a medium of expression.

It is impossible to suggest what the ideal methods of production should be. Every producer acts according to his own convictions and only time will digest the diversity of procedure with which we are confronted today. Even the position of the two fundamentals, the actor and the play, is becoming less clear in view of the influence of the mechanical inventions of this age.

Lighting is an important new development, and it is the purpose of this chapter to indicate the relation of lighting to the various elements of production and to suggest the order in which the details of its application to each particular play should be considered. Each step in the process of application in view of the functions, the qualities, and the technical features of lighting as they are considered from the standpoint of the design of the light plot; the practical working out of the plot in a definite setup of instruments; the development of the cue sheet in rehearsal; and the control of light during the performance is suggested here as a guide, rather than as a rule.

I. PLANS

The first step in the problem is the coordination and design of lighting in relation to the various elements that enter into production. The following details merely indicate the elements to be considered and do not indicate in any way the actual methods of design. In view of the number of individuals concerned in making a production, and its reception by the audience, no rules will ever take the place of the artistic ability of the designer, provided he understands the technical and dramatic problem thoroughly. The coordinated efforts of all the artists that have to do with the theatre depend upon a mutual understanding and agreement between all concerned and a properly related expression of each craft. In view of this, a definite method of procedure should lead up to the problem of the design; and the design in sketch form should be submitted as a practical solution of the visual effects.

A. PROFESSIONAL RELATIONSHIP

The degree to which light can be used in production as a contributing element depends upon the appreciation of lighting on the part of the playwright, producer, designer, and the audience. The knowledge each one has of the other's problem always tends to guarantee a greater coordination of expression than when each goes his own way. The lack of understanding of lighting on the part of these people has relegated it to the hands of the electrician, who has very little authority and the results are correspondingly limited. If there is a conviction on the part of the author, the producer, and the designer that light has a great dramatic value, allowance will be made for its technical limitations.

1. THE PLAYWRIGHT. Instinctive or acquired knowledge of the dramatic possibilities of lighting in relation to the development of the plot of the play.

    Unfortunately the playwright, in establishing the skeleton upon which a production is built, instinctively relies upon lighting only to the extent that he has used it in the past or needs it for effects which have little chance for realization because they do not fall within the characteristics of the instruments nor the methods in use today. The economy of speech in talking pictures illustrates how much more the playwright can depend upon visual effects to convey intellectual and emotional values than in the past. The script indicates the type of play and the style of production.

    a. It contains suggestions for the use of light to give effects of time and place, composition, and mood, but primarily the playwright expects lighting to provide the degree of naturalism which is consistent with his demands on the actor.

    b. It should avoid precise directions for lighting unless they are conceived out of a thorough knowledge of the technical means for achieving a result.

2. THE PRODUCER (Director). It is his duty to make the script of the playwright a living expression before the audience. No play is of the theatre until it is produced. Ideally the producer should be able to determine the application of all the elements of production, so that a complete coordination between the script, the actor, the setting, and the visual effects in their proper relation to each other can be presented to the audience.

    a. For practical reasons, the producer leans on the assistance of several technicians and artists to produce the visual effects and devotes most of his energy to the direction of the actor. In this respect he becomes a director and must rely upon the sympathetic cooperation of his assistants.

    b. He has the responsibility of developing the business and plot of the play to establish a consistent and definite audience-reaction to the mood of the play.

    c. In his eyes the actor is the greatest common denominator between the idea of the author and the audience. He depends upon interpreting the dramatic meaning of the play through selected gesture and movement and by word of mouth. Therefore, to him, giving visibility to the actor's face becomes light's primary function.

3. THE DESIGNER. Similarly to the producer, the designer must depend upon a number of assistants to carry out the plans of the visual effects for which he is responsible. Ideally, he should be equipped artistically to express the suggestions as laid down in the script in relation to the interpretation of the actor and the demands of the director. Beyond this he should be thoroughly acquainted with the technical means of producing all the visual effects and should make his design consistent with the simplest technical means available.

    Practically speaking, the average designer is dependent upon the scene technician, the costumer, the property man, and the electrician; and only as he is able to coordinate their efforts do the visual effects of a production have a unity of expression where no one element is more completely finished than another. Too often through ignorance on the part of the designer the various visual details are not considered in relation to each other.

Lighting in particular, in view of the order of application, suffers most because it is expected to adapt itself to the idea of the play, to give visibility to the actors and atmosphere to the setting, and to pull together the various visual elements which usually have been designed with very little relation to it. In the eyes of the designer the use of light to give the proper composition is its most important function.

a. Scenery. The arrangement and color of the set to determine the style and visual effect of background.

b. Costumes. Color, form, and style.

c. Properties. Arrangement color, and style.

d. Lighting. Application of the functions of light to the production, chiefly naturalism and composition.

4. THE AUDIENCE. The audience's psychological reception of visual effects.

a. Physiological reaction to the qualities of light.

b. Acceptance of conventions of lighting in relation to the limitations due to technical means of expression in light.

c. The illusion and mood created unconsciously by the visual effects, chiefly due to the proper application of the functions of lighting.

B. TYPE OF PLAY

The playwright indicates the type of play in his manuscript. In the chapters on the qualities of light and its functions, the physiological reaction to the various qualities of light and the influences which determine mental reaction can be referred to in determining the lighting which is most practical to apply to the type of play. Most plays combine elements of comedy and tragedy, so that lighting should be designed to enhance the emotional situations throughout the play.

C. THE STYLE OF PRODUCTION

Although indicated by the playwright in his manuscript, the style of production depends upon the interpretation given it by the producer. In terms of lighting, style is the approach which ranges between naturalism and the utterly arbitrary effects of expressionism. The various shadings may very well follow the approach or the method chosen for directing the action of the play.

1. The play with broad sweeps of emotion, generally detached and objective, are formal or classic.

2. Plays of adventure, imagination, and idealism are classed as romantic.

3. The factual approach of more recent years is realistic.

4. The reaction from the naturalistic and factual and the use of symbols which have pure emotional significance is embodied in the expressionistic approach.

D. APPLICATION OF THE FUNCTIONS OF LIGHT

As indicated above, the style of production and the type of play determine the application or use of the functions of lighting. Instinctively the designer should consider all the visual elements as a unit, and particularly the distribution of light in relation to the setting, costumes, and properties. Just as he considers the problem of sight lines, his approach to lighting should be in terms of the technical means of application and he should determine the relative importance of the various functions of light as they are used in the particular play. There is always a disparity in application between the various functions. A related expression of visibility, naturalism, composition, and mood is the ultimate goal for the use of light on the stage.

E. METHODS OF LIGHTING

In view of the technical means of creating light distribution to carry out the functions of light and to coordinate them with the play, direction and the setting, more or less arbitrary practices have developed in order to solve the problem most directly. The necessity for creating the qualities of light through the use of several instruments has made it seem practical to divide the distribution of light over the stage into certain areas and to select various instruments to give a range of the qualities of light to each part—Acting areas, toning and blending on the setting, background areas, and special distributions to give accent, motivation or special effects.

F. SCENE DESIGN

The pictorial effect of the setting with a suggestion of the distribution and color of light for each scene in the play. Generally the designer makes a sketch of only one situation in each scene, usually without consideration of the technical means of accomplishing the lighting. He does, however, consider most of the practical problems of the structural arrangements of the setting and the general style of production, and allows a certain flexibility for unforseen changes which may be necessary in the form and color. Either the lighting effect desired should be indicated or the sketch should represent simply a decorator's elevation.

1. The sketch. The light distribution for each scene in color. Indication of motivation and composition. Scenes within scenes often warrant additional sketches.

2. The plan. Plan of the set and its architectural relation to the rest of the building or locality if any. Orientation with regard to direction of sun or moon if used.

3. The use of a model. A practical method of determining the direct solution of the various changes of distribution in plastic state. Use of model instruments. The ability to approximate only the final effects, the danger of overemphasizing pictorial effect, and the slighting of the problem of visibility. Use of dolls in costume. Minute study of detail in relation to full-scale problems.

4. Consideration of practical features.

    a. Masking of instruments, sight lines.

    b. Positions for mounting instruments—beams, cyclorama, inner proscenium, etc.

    c. Color of the motivating source determines the color and direction of the acting area units. Emphasis and composition. Variety from scene to scene.

G. TECHNICAL CONSIDERATIONS

The problem of rigging scenery so that it can be quickly shifted has developed certain practices which are intimately connected with the problem of mounting and controlling instruments. The fly space over the stage and various positions about the floor must be shared by scenery and instruments together, so that there must be coordination between the handling of the scenery and the positions in which the instruments must be used. This problem has been the reason for the development of rigging methods and the allocation of certain traditional positions for lighting instruments.

1. The mounting of instruments should be such that no accidental jar caused by the shifting scenery is liable to change their direction or cause them to fall; and at the same time it should permit their quick removal for the shifts of the scenery in case they happen to be in the way.

2. The size of instruments and mounting apparatus has been designed to limit the space occupied by them. Bulky apparatus, no matter how efficient, becomes a liability rather than an asset.

3. Clear space at the teaser, the tormentors, in the flies and in the rigging of the scenery must be carefully considered so as not to block the path of the rays of light.

4. Permanently mounted instruments which are part of the rigging of the scenery, on a revolving or wagon stage, or on a set flown as a unit, should be rigidly mounted and provisions made for making and breaking the connections.

H. ROUTINE PRACTICE

In summary, where the different elements involved in the coordination of the design stage are in the hands of various people, an agreement is necessary before the actual working out of the plans can be started. These steps are of course, dependent upon the routine of procedure in each theatre and are apt to vary with each type of production within the same organization. However, in general, the production staff should be constantly in touch with one another so that there is a general agreement before a start is made.

1. Plans. Discussion of the type of play, and style of production in view of the available equipment, actors, and general program of production. Detailed analysis of each mood situation the play and the general plan of business, either indicated in the script or decided upon by the producer or director. Establishment of acting areas.

2. Budget. A general estimate of the cost of each division of a production. Allow for 25 to 50 percent in excess of estimates for contingencies.

3. Submission of sketches and plans. Scenery, costume, technical elements, and lighting scheme. Make adjustments necessary to coordinate them. Acceptance of plans.

II. DEVELOPMENT

A finished production involving numerous technical problems depends upon a successful coordination of all details. The relationship is far more important than the finish or perfection of each part. In any problem of expression in the fine arts, particularly that which is not being done by any one individual, the result depends considerably upon the complete understanding and cooperation of all the individuals concerned.

No matter how well the plans are laid or how sincere the various individuals are in their effort to cooperate, a number of unpredictable problems may arise in the development of the final expression. For this reason, a certain amount of flexibility or fluidity of plan should be allowed for. Some elements are more easily changed than others; and, fortunately or unfortunately, particularly due to its order of application, lighting is expected to be the most flexible of all the various elements.

Ideally speaking, in view of the inflexible nature of the technical means of expression, it might be well to have a completely lighted set on the stage before the director begins to work out his business with the actors. In this way, it would be possible to coordinate the lighting with the actors in the most practical manner and eventually this will be necessary if light is to be used to accompany the entire action of the play.

The practical problem today requires the scene designer, or more particularly the lighting designer, to follow the development of all the parts that are influenced or concerned in his plan for lighting the stage. The assembling of the instruments, scenery, and all the visual elements is necessary before any lighting can be done.

A. LAYOUT

The preparation of the layout drawing deals with the selection and location of instruments in view of the available structural features for mounting. It is based on the technical problem of lighting with electricity and the method by which the functions of light are applied to the particular production. Generally speaking, only the floor instruments can be moved about easily. The ideal situation rests in the selection of the fewest instruments which give a range of the qualities of light necessary for each scene in the play, from fixed positions. This obviously requires a certain conventional use of light and limits the flexibility which might be desirable. Some theatres are equipped to provide almost any direction of throw by elaboration of the number of instruments, but normally speaking the best practice is to select a specific group of instruments and to mount them in the best positions for each production.

1. <u>Lamp wattage.</u> For each position in relation to the maximum demand for output in view of the length of throw, the coefficient of transmission of the various color mediums, the type of instrument, and the cutoffs used. Change of focus alters intensity.

2. <u>Color mediums.</u> Must hold generally throughout each scene or unless remotely controlled, must then be changed by hand. Generally, it is wise to have a set of colors necessary for each instrument or for a group of adjacent instruments stored in a box nearby. If the instrument is inaccessible, as it sometimes is in the beams or on the balcony front, that color must be selected which is serviceable throughout several scenes, or as many instruments as there are changes of color at each position must be used.

3. <u>Type of instrument and position.</u> Selection of the instrument in relation to the distribution desired and the service it can render throughout the various scenes by variability in focus, direction, changes in color or intensity. Provision for mounting the instrument. Area to be covered. Accessories to be used.

4. <u>Control.</u> Consideration of the ability of the operator and his crew. Flexibility of the switchboard, the degree of complexity in changes which can be achieved satisfactorily. Consideration of changes between scenes. Time allowed, and accuracy.

5. The layout drawing. In view of the above, the layout working drawings generally include:

   a. A plan at 1/4- or 1/2-inch scale. Use symbols to indicate the type of instrument, its size, location and general direction. Give each instrument a number that refers to the schedule and sometimes a name to indicate the area lighted, the number of the color and control.

   b. A section and sometimes a rear elevation of the proscenium are advisable to show how position affects the angles or directions of the light rays. This shows the mounting height primarily.

   c. A schedule of equipment listing:

      1. The plan number of the instrument.

      2. Its type (including manufacturer's number).

      3. Its wattage.

      4. Its use.

      5. Its accessories.

      6. Its color for each scene (including diffusers).

      7. Its position (height also).

      8. Its connection (to pocket or dimmer or both). Plugging boxes and cable lengths.

      9. Any notes which concern changes from scene to scene.

B. DIRECTING

The practice of establishing the business of a play with the actors on a bare stage under work lights invariably is so involved by the mere mechanics of directing that lighting in particular receives little or no consideration. With the lighting scheme well in mind, the director will automatically consider the use of motivating light for visibility and the most direct means of obtaining effects by the available instruments when working out acting positions and business on the bare stage. It is difficult to unravel complicated business on the stage after it is once set, so the designer, electrician, or stage manager should check each bit of new business in relation to the plans for lighting. The practice of attempting to light a show in dress rehearsal is the chief reason for the crude results that are sometimes seen today. Only by means of the lighting rehearsal and careful coordination with the directing during dress rehearsals can the desired results be approached.

C. WORKING DRAWINGS

The working drawings of the setting (plan, section, and elevation) should consider the problem of mounting, directing, and masking the various instruments. Even though a great deal of accidental success may be achieved, when only the conventional means of lighting are provided, really satisfactory results can be obtained only when working drawings consider the use of the available instruments and methods of lighting.

D. BUILDING

Careful observation of the development of the setting and the properties allows for handling of instruments in relation to scene changes and the provisions for mounting and directing instruments. The location of braces, battens, and openings, and even the storage of scenery between scenes, often affects the positions of instruments.

E. PAINTING

The relation between the necessary color of motivating light and the pigment used on the setting and the properties indicate that where there is any question of color, scenery should be tried under the colored light to be used, as well as under white light. On the other hand, the final effect on all parts of the stage affects the appearance of each part to such an extent that individual tests do not mean much. Allowance for changes by the use of stippled surfaces obviates this problem considerably.

F. DYEING

Costumes should undergo the same process. Cheap materials which should appear rich under the various colors of light are generally used. Very often the designs of costumes, in following a certain color composition, are entirely at odds with the color of the motivating light which must be used, so that some provision for picking them up in the colors of light from the toning and blending instruments should be provided for. Shading and dipping costumes in various dyes to give high light and shade help to increase the effect of the lighting.

G. RIGGING THE STAGE

Under given conditions of hanging apparatus and stage space, a certain amount of the rigging of the scenery and the allocation of stacking space can be made on paper. It should be thoroughly coordinated with the plans for rigging and mounting the instruments. Very often the technical problems of rigging and moving scenery complicate the problem of mounting instruments. Book ceilings and slack snatch lines very often foul overhead hanging instruments. Stage braces, jacks, etc., often occupy the space useful for stand lamps and floor strips. The hanging marine cable which feeds the borders is always a hazard.

H. MOUNTING THE INSTRUMENTS

After the plan of the layout has been thoroughly organized, the instruments and accessories should be gathered together, cleaned and made ready for mounting. Mounting apparatus should consider dependability of position and yet allow for adjustment of focus and direction and change of color medium and accessories as may be necessary from scene to scene. All joints, clamps, etc., should be sticky or tight, and under no conditions should the mounting be such that the instruments or their accessories are liable to be knocked loose if accidentally hit by a piece of scenery. The instrument should also be accessible so that lamps and color mediums can be changed when necessary, and connections should all be tight so that there is no failure or flickering of the lamp.

1. Put in the lamp and see that it is on the optical axis and in good condition. Check the position of the reflector. Test.

2. Mount the instrument securely on the batten, base, or stand and screw down the set bolts so that its position is secure (not so tightly that threads are stripped or the shank cracked).

3. Make the connections at the lamp, at the feed pocket, and if necessary at the switchboard, in relation to the capacity, the color, area lighted, and any cue for which it may be used.

4. Put on the accessories, such as funnels, louvers, or cutoffs. Make them secure.

5. Focus the instrument on the area to be covered.

6. Put in the color medium, cut off and diffuser, if any.

I. CODE

Check the layout of equipment in accordance with the requirements of the Code from the standpoint of capacity, suitability for use, mechanical strength, insulation, heating effects, and arcing effects—connectors, cable, pockets, dimmers, switches, fuses.

III. REHEARSAL

When all the instruments and all the details of the setting are assembled and arranged according to the predetermined plan, it is possible to start lighting the scene. Generally the stage space with its setting can be considered a void until light is brought into it, and the application of the various functions of light can then be worked out by balancing intensity, color, form, and movement. This process is most practically worked out in the light rehearsal. It is a slow procedure, due usually to the inability of the operator to see effects that he is creating by throwing switches and regulating dimmers. After the preliminary setup is made in lighting rehearsal and the various cues rehearsed, all is ready for dress rehearsal. The inclusion of the actor requires a certain amount of adjustment to bring the coordination down to a finished expression. And by the time of the final dress rehearsal (ordinarily there should be several) a unified presentation of the plans should have been developed.

A. FUNCTIONS

The relative importance and the degree of application of each function of lighting in expressing the visual aspects of the style of production for each type of play must be thoroughly allocated in the mind of the designer or lighting specialist. The degree of visibility for each part of setting, particularly the acting area, must be assured. For realistic productions, naturalism is the dominant function, and motivated lighting is the standard to which the rest of the lighting must be balanced. The aim to produce naturalism must be tempered with a selection of colors and distributions which give dramatic emphasis and composition to the stage picture. Finally in this process of developing the lighting for a particular scene, the visual effect should convey the proper dramatic atmosphere or mood.

B. THE LIGHTING REHEARSAL

With the foregoing in mind, the regulation of the lighting or the balancing of intensity, color and form in order to create the desired illusion for each scene most effectively, should be undertaken at a definitely-appointed rehearsal, and should be made in relation to the visual effects as seen by the audience. Ordinarily, time for lighting rehearsal is at a premium, and generally the compromises necessary, due to the regulation of lighting at the last moment, are the reason for the conventional effects of lighting seen in the average production, and as a result, the feeling of conscious tolerance on the part of the audience.

When it is not possible for the operator to see clearly the effects he is producing, it is necessary for the designer or lighting man to sit in the auditorium during the lighting rehearsal and, perhaps by means of a telephone or shouted directions, to interpret vaguely his feelings to the switchboard operator, so that the latter can regulate the lighting to produce the various effects desired. A great deal of time and feeling are lost in this translation of ideas into mechanical terms. Eventually perhaps the lighting designer will set dimmer readings directly without depending upon an assistant on the board.

In the lighting rehearsal time should be allowed for the recording of a preliminary setup, and a rehearsal of cues.

1. Preliminary setup. Be sure to have all the visual elements except the actor present. It is wise even to test out the costumes for the various scenes under the setup before arriving at a final decision. The stage manager can be very helpful during lighting rehearsal by moving through the various bits of business to determine whether the visibility on the acting area is proper for all situations during the scene. An estimated setup on paper, if simple, tends to save time during rehearsal.

    a. Starting with all lights out, (for realistic effect) bring up the motivating lights on dimmer to approximately the ultimate intensity. Balance the brightness of the remaining instruments to create a compositional effect.

    b. Check the distribution of lighting on the acting area in the important positions, as determined during the acting rehearsals, with the stage manager.

    c. When the final pictorial effect is satisfactory from the standpoint of visibility, naturalism, composition, and mood, register the set-up on the cue sheet.

    d. Make a preliminary setup for each scene of the play and take readings.

    e. Mark the position and direction of instruments.

    f. Record all colors, positions, and connections as they are determined for each scene, on the layout sheet. Any change in direction or position from scene to scene, should also be noted.

2. Cues. Changes in lighting, either as time cues running over a certain period in the scene, line cues which are established by definite speeches or cues depending upon bits of business during the course of the scene, should be rehearsed during the lighting rehearsal and the operations at the switchboard arranged so that cues can be accomplished most effectively.

    a. For line or business cues a warning should be given either by an action or a line spoken by the actor or by signals from the stage manager; and the dead cue should be taken likewise, either on the action, line, or from the stage manager. The latter is the practice in the professional theatre.

    b. Time cues, which run over a period of time, as for example, sunsets, should have station points which indicate the proportional dimming at certain periods during the progress of change.

    c. Preliminary readings, station points, and final readings should be recorded on the cue sheet. Any mechanical change in the operating levers and switches should also be noted.

3. <u>Curtain Cues.</u> The arbitrary method of starting the scene should be as consistent as possible with the dramatic effects desired. Raising or drawing the act curtain is one of the
most firmly-established conventions of the theatre and tends not only to arouse the expectancy of the audience but to limit the continued emotional reaction throughout the complete
progress of the play. The elimination of seeing the movement of the curtain often tends
to increase the illusion, especially when the lights required for the stage picture are
brought from "out" to "reading" simultaneously after the curtain is up. The transition
from house lights to stage lights must be very carefully timed.

   a. Start dimming the house lights then; bring up the foots (or curtain lights) to illuminate
   the curtain and to call attention to the stage.

   b. When the house is out, signal the stage manager. Bring the foots (or curtain lights)
   to "reading" immediately, as the curtain goes up or opens.

   c. When the curtain is fully open, dim on the front lights quickly.

   d. Reverse the process when the curtain is lowered.

   e. For curtain calls and for the applause, keep the house out until signalled by stage
   manager, but always leave some light either on the stage or on the curtain. Bright-
   ening up stage lights for curtain calls tends to increase the applause.

   f. Between scenes bring up the house to a little over half and have foots or front lights
   on the curtain. For quick changes do not bring up the house lights.

   g. Never let the audience be without some illumination for more than thirty seconds.

4. <u>Scene changes.</u> Must be made quickly and accurately. The manner in which instruments
are handled and the changes necessary on the switchboard setup, always determine the
elaboration of the layout which is practical. Compromises in the ideal control of light
must always be made with the human and technical elements involved. Provision must be
made for changing color mediums, refocusing or changing the position of the instruments.
Crew assignments to those temperamentally and physically equipped to act with precision.
When "Strike" is called:

   a. Turn on the work light, and start resetting the board. Care must be taken not to cut
   the house lights or to turn on any front lights.

   b. Shift all instruments in the way of striking the set and set for new scene as soon as
   possible.

   c. Turn on all lights that need to be focused.

   d. Check the board setup.

   e. Signal stage manager when ready.

5. <u>Adjustments.</u> Throughout all this process, certain adjustments in position, focus, color,
and type of distribution as given by various instruments must be made. The experimentation necessary to make these adjustments requires far more time than is generally allowed, and ordinarily it is wiser to make a sketch setup for each scene in the first lighting
rehearsal, and make the adjustments necessary before the time allotted for the next.

C. COSTUME PARADE

It is often wise, particularly in costume plays, to test out the costumes and make-up under
the colors of light that are set up for each scene. Adjustments in color mediums, make-up,
and dye can be made before dress rehearsal in this manner, thus saving a great deal of time.

D. TECHNICAL REHEARSAL

Technical rehearsal serves as a means of rehearsing the changes from scene to scene, and also any cues that may be involved within the scene. It is particularly valuable for the rehearsal of curtain lights. Although it does not alter the condition of the cue sheet as a rule, it irons out the problem of coordination between the various technical elements. This may be combined with a walk-through or business rehearsal, where the actors go through all their actions and business with only the lines necessary for technical cues and handling properties.

E. DRESS REHEARSALS

Having developed the cue sheet to this point, the coordination must be further carried out in connection with the complete action of the play. The stage manager takes charge and performance discipline should hold. Nothing disrupts the effectiveness of dress rehearsal as much as the time taken to make adjustments in the lighting, although it is sometimes possible during the progress of the rehearsal to regulate distributions from the switchboard as directed by telephone in the auditorium or from the wings, and to coordinate the timing of changes on the board with the progress of the play. As far as possible, the dress rehearsal should be conducted in the same terms as performance, starting with the house lights and proceeding through each scene in the order in which they occur.

1. Stage manager. The stage manager becomes the director of all mechanics of the stage, and all cues and changes involved in the smooth running of the rehearsal should be centered in his authority. Signals should be transmitted by means of phones or lights rather than buzzers. Curtain calls should be rehearsed.

2. Coordination. The timing of all changes should be coordinated with the business on the stage. Allowance should be made for unavoidable errors or dropping of lines on the part of the actor. Distributions, particularly intensities and colors in toning and blending instruments, should be adjusted to coordinate with the action of the play and changes should be recorded on the cue sheet. Any complicated cues should be rehearsed several times in order to guarantee perfect timing.

3. Discipline. The switchboard operator becomes in a sense an actor from this point on and he should learn the routine or changes on the switchboard both during the scene and between scenes, more or less in the same terms as the actor learns his lines. He must pay constant attention to the operation of the switchboard, take precaution against failures, check all readings, and expedite shifts. He should be constantly in touch with the stage manager by signal or telephone.

4. Adjustments. Minor adjustments can be made during the progress of the dress rehearsal. Major adjustments, such as changing the position of instruments, should be made between dress rehearsals and all changes should be recorded on the cue sheet. Major changes should be tried out with the other instruments used in the scene, in order to see that the combined effect will be satisfactory. No changes after final dress rehearsal.

F. LIGHT PLOT AND CUE SHEET

By the time the next to last dress rehearsal is over, the light plot and cue sheet should have been developed. Only very minor changes should be made without rehearsal. All the adjustments and changes that were made from the preliminary setup to the final dress rehearsal seem necessary in order to achieve complete coordination. In its final form, the cue sheet normally involves all the necessary directions for changes on the switchboard and the light plot is a tabulation of all the elements that are necessary for the reproduction of the play at some future time. This latter includes a layout plan and that which is strictly called the cue sheet. The following outline includes the details that should be recorded on the light plot. The cue sheet generally only includes the last two items.

1. A layout sheet and schedule of instruments.

2. Master setup of switchboard.

3. Dimmer readings.

4. Cues:

   Time—start and finish with station points.
   Line or business—warning and dead cue.
   Readings of dimmers at beginning and end, and any change in switching.

IV. PERFORMANCE

A complete expression of the plans worked out in rehearsal should be the goal of the control of lighting during performances. The operator in a sense is an actor from the entrance of the audience to its exit, from the first performance to the last. A smooth, finished performance is the highest form of professional expression and every precaution should be taken to provide a complete coordination of all the parts of production, to guarantee a dependability which is essential in professional practice, and to continue the excellence of performance even to the point of increased refinement. From the standpoint of lighting, concerning which the audience has very little knowledge of the technical problems, it is more essential to avoid mistakes than in almost any other part in the production. An audience understands the frailities of human nature on the part of the actor, and is not so much distracted as amused when he makes a mistake. But their ignorance of the technical problem of lighting makes a failure or mistake take on an importance that is more distracting than one which is understood.

A. OPERATION

A constant coordination of lighting with the play. Constant contact with the stage manager.

1. Accuracy. When the operator is in a position to see the effects of operating the switch-board, the precise setup of the light plot can be checked visually, otherwise every other means of checking should be taken to guarantee accuracy.

2. Timing. Cues should be timed absolutely to coordinate with the business on the stage. The variability in timing due to differences in the conduct of the actor from performance to performance should be allowed for, thus limiting the exactitude of player-role-timing. Smooth and accurate manipulation produces a convincing effect on the audience.

3. Scene changes. Dispatch is often paramount but speed without precision is useless.

4. Errors. Allowance for mistakes on the part of the actor and failures in the mechanical layout.

B. PRECAUTIONS

The extension of control of the operator through technical means brings into the problem the possibilities of mechanical failure as well as the inevitability of human error. From this point of view a check should be made on the following details before a performance in order to guarantee smooth running.

1. Fuses. Accessible and of the proper capacity.

2. Lamps. Relatively new and not liable to fail at a crucial point. Tight in the socket. Lamps often fail when being turned on, although sometimes in the course of the scene they may die, with correspondingly distracting results.

3. Circuits. Test each circuit before each performance. Cable connections should always be tested before each performance.

4. Colors. Color mediums (gelatin) fade and are easily broken. They should be examined

before each performance, to see that they are in satisfactory condition.

5. <u>Focus.</u> Many instruments require very delicate focusing and are often subject to knocks in the movement of scenery. In as far as possible their position and direction should be marked so that they can be brought back to focus at any time.

6. <u>Cues.</u> Cues should be rehearsed just as are special scenes in the play, until they are absolutely timed.

C. MAINTENANCE

All apparatus should be kept up to date. Color mediums and lamps, cables, etc., should be changed as they show signs of failure or wear during use. Inasmuch as most of the early performances are often little more than dress rehearsals, continued refinement of the lighting and its manipulation should be undertaken with each performance. A more careful timing of cues; more subtle regulation of dimming, particularly from the standpoint of proportionality; greater speed in making changes between scenes; a more careful focusing of the instruments; and even a complete relighting of the several situations in the play in relation to the reaction of the audience should be considered as the play goes on in performance from day to day.

APPENDIX I.

HISTORY

In order to take advantage of the research and developments of the past, to understand the present situation, and to anticipate the developments of the future, the student should be acquainted with the history of stage lighting. The invention of the electric lamp gave such an impetus to attempts to use light dramatically that by far the most important era falls within modern times. However, the history of the part light has played in relation to dramatic production reaches back to the beginning of the theatre.

When electricity eliminated some of the shortcomings of the candle and gas periods, it became possible to use artificial light for the first time in simulation of natural light. In spite of the complications of electricity and instruments the public is becoming aware of the functions of light beyond that of giving visibility. Undoubtedly new methods for producing artificial light will further eliminate technical problems and the designer will begin to use light more as an art in itself. By that time we may have developed a light sense much as we have at present a musical sense, and it will be much more practical than the latter because while we can exist without music, existence would be difficult without light.

I. OUTDOOR THEATRES AND FESTIVALS

A. GREEK AND ROMAN

Daylight and sunlight gave the effect of absolute reality. Torches and oil lamps were the only artificial light sources, so that most dramatic productions were held during the daytime. However, the audience was educated to accept the convention of symbols suggesting the condition of the natural elements such as night, fire, storm, etc.

B. THE MEDIEVAL AND RENAISSANCE PERIOD

About the Romanesque and Byzantine theatre there is little known, except that the court fetes of Justinian in Constantinople were supposed to have been elaborately lighted by torches and oil lamps. They seem to have used gold reflectors and colored lights.

The Medieval theatre consisted chiefly of court plays, pageants, and displays in the open. Mystery plays and pageants in the cathedrals were lighted by candles and the dim-colored light created by stained glass windows. The effects must have been unconsciously very dramatic, and very essential to the emotional appeal of the play.

During the Renaissance there was extensive use of display lighting in court fetes (for example, the Boboli Gardens at Florence) and pageants. Buildings such as St. Peter's and the Palazzo Vecchio are still lighted on occasion much as they were in this period. Shakespeare used signs and symbols in his early courtyard productions to give the locale, and often took pains to indicate through his characters the time of day and place of a scene. Paladio's theatre, and a number of others in Italy, first took the theatre out of the uncertain weather conditions into a building under a roof.

II. THE EARLY INDOOR THEATRE

Putting a roof over the theatre overcame the uncertainty of weather conditions and created the demand for artificial light to give visibility. From this time on the history of stage lighting is primarily the story of the development of new lights, sources, and instruments and the attempts to use them dramatically. Just how far these developments influenced methods of production, the design of scenery, and even the technique of playwriting is difficult to say, but it is interesting to note that beyond natural changes of civilization and culture the raw materials of these branches of the theatre are the same today as they were four hundred years ago; but lighting and the technical arts have developed constantly.

A. CANDLELIGHT. SEVENTEENTH CENTURY.

Chandeliers, then concealed strips or rows of lights mark the first development.

B. OIL LAMP. EIGHTEENTH CENTURY

Chimneys on lamps permitted greatly-increased intensity.

C. GASLIGHT PERIOD. UP TO 1879. LIMELIGHT AND ARC.

Gas jet to Welsbach Burner. Yellowish light. Heat, fire hazard, bad acoustics, fumes, smoke, were some of the problems that the use of gas presented. Code regulations attempted to provide protection and their effect carried over into the electric lamp period. Strips of small jets continued the convention of border lights, wing lights, and footlights. The gas table—a series of valve dimmers comprised the first centralized control board. Master control and smoothness of dimming were its chief advantages. Gaslight influenced the color of scenery and make-up.

The calcium or limelight was invented by Drummond in 1803, but was not used on the stage until 1860. It gave a high powered white light and was used with reflectors and lenses for spotting. Constant adjustment required an operator, who often had to carry on his back the cumbersome oxygen and hydrogen tanks which produced the flame by playing on a stick of lime—hence "lime-light".

D. BEGINNINGS OF ELECTRICITY IN THE THEATRE

The arc was invented in 1809 by Sir Humphrey Davy. By 1879 it was traditional to use the lime-light and the electric arc as single, high-powered light sources. It made greater amounts of illumination economical. It was adapted in the same form as earlier light sources and continued the convention of general illumination, given by borderlights, wing lights, and footlights. The incandescent lamp was developed by Edison and Swan in 1879.

III. THE MODERN THEATRE. 1880, THE ELECTRIC INCANDESCENT LAMP

The indefinite artistic problem of using light in harmony with a play and the variability in setting, costumes, and make-up have tended to limit the application of scientific lighting in the theatre. The great flexibility required in controlling structural features and apparatus has established a technical problem whose solution depends upon a knowledge of the requirements of production. Few producers are able to state their desires in technical terms so that the engineer can work out a satisfactory solution. As a result, rule-of-thumb methods belying any scientific approach persist.

The use of light in all its qualities in the theatre, where the visual process must be unconscious and certainly not dictated by the technical means employed, presents a problem in lighting which is so complicated that the approach from the standpoint of the designer-technician is the only one that seems practical. The future of lighting depends upon the ability of the designer to understand the technical problem involved in the use of light, to apply the developments the engineer has made in other fields, and to specify the exact needs which only the engineer can provide.

Inasmuch as the invention of the incandescent lamp established the beginning of the most productive era in the history of stage lighting, the various important fields of development are traced independently of each other.

A. DESIGNERS AND PRODUCERS AND THEIR CONTRIBUTIONS TO STAGE LIGHTING

  1. Richard Wagner. Created a demand for extensive technical developments.

  2. Gordon Craig. Revolted against the conventions of the theatre and demanded use of light and scenery as compositional elements with the play.

  3. Adolph Appia. Defined the stage in terms of time and space and suggested the use of light to create mood and composition.

4. Steele MacKaye. Producer and actor. Developed the effect machine. Designed many mechanical contrivances for the theatre. Was an arch-realist. Made plans for the great Spectatorium of the Chicago World's Fair, 1893.

5. Henry Irving. Experimented with effects of realism. Colored lights. Sectional use of strips and borders. Light rehearsals.

6. Mario Fortuny. Developed the Kuppelhorizont, or dome, and the system of lighting which used reflectors made of movable colored-silk panels.

7. David Belasco. Abolished footlights and used lights from the auditorium. Developed a standard of realism through his electrician, Louis Hartmann.

8. Max Reinhardt. Applied the principles of Craig and Appia and used light as a dramatic medium. One of the foremost practical showmen.

9. Linnebach and Hasait. Discarded the Fortuny system and invented the rolling cyclorama and other technical features to facilitate production.

10. Jessner, Pirchan, Passetti, Stern, Strnad, and a number of other European designers and producers. Stressed the decorative quality of light.

11. Meyerhold and Tairoff and the Russian Theatre. Used light as a purely arbitrary dramatic medium.

12. Simonson, Geddes, Jones, Oenslager, Mielziner, Short, Johnson, and other designers in the American theatre. Have made extensive use of light as a design element.

13. Thomas Wilfred. Invented the Clavilux. A light organ that demonstrates the use of light as an art in itself.

14. Rosenthal, Clark, Musser, Feder, Elson, Harvey and Watson are lighting specialists who practice their profession as members of the scenic designers union.

B. OTHER INFLUENCES

1. Playwrights. Have through all the ages, particularly in the modern, indicated the use of light in the presentation of their plays, for its dramatic value.

2. The Little Theatre and University Theatre. Through high ideals but generally with inadequate equipment, they are educating the public to the dramatic functions of lighting.

3. The Motion-Picture Presentation House and the Revue Theatre. Through the arbitrary use of light in full colors they have demonstrated the public's acceptance and desire for the decorative qualities of light and "trick" effects.

4. Equipment Companies. Have endeavored to supply the demand for equipment as it arises. Recently experimentation and scientific research have produced equipment with far greater efficiency and control than ever before.

5. Photographers. Have made pictures with natural and artificial lighting that often serve as an example of excellence in creating an arbitrary composition.

6. T-V. The enormous development of this form of production has given great impetus to the development of equipment and control apparatus. Much of this can be used in theatrical as well as T-V production.

APPENDIX II.

PSYCHOLOGY

An understanding of the physical properties of light on the part of the designer must be accompanied by a general knowledge of the elements of visual reaction considered under the heading of psychology. In the theatre all lighting is planned to serve the audience, therefore the manner in which the observer reacts to light determines the design of stage lighting. Psychology is not an exact science, but through it we can apply approximate rules of procedure and draw certain broad conclusions.

By far the most important function of lighting on the stage is to assist in creating an unconscious, convincing reaction of dramatic quality on the audience. The eye has special characteristics which determine the qualities of light through sensory stimuli. As it is the only practical gateway through which light can reach the mind, the designer's problem is to create the physical stimuli which provide the visual perception elements. The organization of these stimuli into definite mental reactions takes place involuntarily in the mind of the observer. Thus, through a knowledge of psychology of vision he can provide the selected visual elements which help to convey the meaning of the play. See any simple college text on psychology, particularly the chapters on sensation and vision.

I. THE EYE

Inasmuch as the eye has certain physiological characteristics which determine the extent of sensation, an understanding of its parts and methods of operation assists in analyzing the elements of the sensation of vision.

A. PARTS

The eye is like a camera set in a hollow pocket in the bony structure of the head on each side of the bridge of the nose. Its various parts consist of:

1. The outer membrane is opaque white except the transparent front part, which is called the cornea.

2. Immediately back of the cornea is the Iris, a variously-colored membrane, having in its center an adjustable round opening, called the pupil.

3. Behind the iris lies a lens, which is adjusted in thickness for focal length by muscular action.

4. The body of the eye is filled with a fibrous transparent substance called vitreous humor.

5. The inside coating of the eye is called the retina. It is made up of a mosiac of minute nerves and fibres in the form of rods and cones. At one point in the retina, directly back of the lens, there is a predominance of cones which is called the fovia or yellow spot. Not far from this and toward the nose where the optic nerve enters, there are no rods or cones and it is therefore not sensitive to light rays. This is called the blind spot.

B. METHODS OF OPERATION

The light passes through the cornea, the pupil, the lens and the vitreous humor to the retina which is similar to the sensitive plate in a camera, and forms a pattern or image. This stimulates the end fibres of the optic nerve, and thereby sets up nerve impulses which are transmitted to the brain.

1. The Iris. Adaptation. Within certain limits, the iris is able to determine the amount of light that reaches the eye. 2-8 millimeters variable opening. 1-16 in area. Acts involuntarily to the average brightness in the field of vision.

2. The Lens. Accommodation. The involuntary adjustment of the lens in thickness or focal

length.   At rest when thin or when it has a long focal length.

3.   Vitreous Humor.   This substance filling the body of the eye is supposed to transmit the rays as a transparent substance.   Undoubtedly it has some influence on color reaction in that it is found to give certain luminescent effects.   Chemical reaction.

4.   The Retina.   Sensitive to light rays at varying degrees over its entire area, but sharply sensitive at the yellow spot and not at all at its blind spot.   Time for resolution of an image.   Simultaneous contrasts are enforced.

5.   Binocular Vision and Muscular Action.   Space relationships.

II. SENSATION

Being aware of something is due to the messages sent to the mind usually by more than one sense. This always complicates analyzation because stimuli generally occur simultaneously.   Ultimately the determination of a perception depends upon the selection and creation of stimuli in view of their distinguishable differences or qualities.

Any stimulation of the sense organs or receptors from an outside influence, such as radient energy, chemical action, pressure, etc., if of sufficient intensity, causes a sensation.   Receptors are the sensory organs which supply contact with the outside world and are of such special classes that they respond to stimulation generally of only one type.   While the skin is sensitive to heat radiation, the eye is stimulated only by radiations within the visual octave. The limits of sensation of any sense (vision for instance) determine the extent of design of sense stimuli.   Thus, our reaction to light through the sense of vision determines the qualities of light.

A.   INTENSITY OR BRIGHTNESS

The amount of stimulation from threshold to the saturation limit, from the lowest limits where we are conscious of light energy to the highest where complete saturation takes place and fatigue sets in, determines the range of intensity in light.   The characteristic reactions of the eye over this range and the elements which determine the amount of intensity which reaches the eye can be considered separately.

1.   Threshold visibility.   .001 foot-candles.   Lamberts.

2.   Comfortable Range.   Acuity.   Foot-candle tables.

3.   Saturation takes place in cases of excessive illumination.   Action of the iris in the eye tends to protect the retina and to decrease the effect of illumination from threshold to full saturation.   13,000 f.c., daylight and sunlight.

4.   Amount of radiation that reaches the eye is dependent upon the brightness of the object.

B.   QUALITY OR COLOR

The general modality of stimulation which is characteristic of a particular sense; the kind which distinguishes between certain parts of the stimulation, such as the varying wave length of light; and the specific kind which allows the selection of degrees of the parts in relation to each other, as the shades and tints of color; define the quality of sensation.

1.   Primary Colors—red, green and blue.

2.   Hues, tints, and shades.   Composite result.

3.   The color of the light illuminating the object or the additive effect of all the wave lengths illuminating the object, combined with the selective reflection offered by the pigment on the surface of the object, determines the resultant wave lengths that reach the eye.

119

4. Sensitivity or Luminosity Curve.

5. Color Contrasts.

C. EXTENSITY OR FORM

This is the dimension of sensation, the size and the position of sensation on the retina. The individual nerve-end fibres, each subtending about one minute of a degree in the retina, are able to assimilate sensations on the retina and the sum total of the sensations is transmitted to the mind in the form of an image with a shape and position in relation to the observer. Thus, localized stimulations lead to space delineation and space consciousness, but closely allied with this are the patterns in intensity and color and the motor or muscular action that establish the size, shape, position, and movement of an object in space.

1. The lens of the eye forms a two-dimensional image on the retina.

2. Signs of Space Perception.

    a. Relative sharpness of outline.

    b. Superposition

    c. Direction of shadows.

    d. Form of light and shade.

    e. Lines of perspective.

    f. Relative motion.

    g. Scale.

    h. Relative color.

3. Patterns of brightness and color differences.

D. DURATION OR MOVEMENT

The time required for accommodation and adaptation in forming sharp images on the eye and the muscular action of focusing or directing the eye on various subjects, involves a certain amount of involuntary movement. The changes of distribution of light coming to the eye have the same effect, and these changes as determined by the designer can give a sense of vitality in the visual field that is similar to nature in its subtle changes during the time of day. Or he can arbitrarily change the appearance of otherwise static objects through a series of patterns and colors that remove them from their normal realistic state.

1. Time required for adaptation and accommodation.

2. Changes in the intensity, color, and form of light alter the normal appearance of an object as it ordinarily appears under static lighting. The movement of trees waving in the breeze or objects as they cross our field of vision change the pattern of light on the retina. The actor moving about the stage.

III. PERCEPTION

Perception appears to take place as the result of sense stimulations and the apperceptive process organizes or synthesizes them into a mental picture. Experience, association, judgment, will, interest, and abstract appeal are influences which prejudice the formation of every perception. Every individual instinctively reacts to the stimulation of sensation through all the senses according to these factors in varying degrees. Up to a certain point the reaction is universal and all concepts are somewhat the same. Beyond this point each individual, due to what we call his physical make-up and background (which determine the above variables), has a different perception of an outside stimulus. Even to a given set of conditions, the same individual will react differently from time to time.

We seldom gain a complete sensation through one sense alone. Sight is influenced by sound and sound by sight. Human reaction is too involved to be determined exactly. Yet, in proportion as we allow for the various influences that affect the perception process, we are less apt to make mistakes in application.

A. EXPERIENCE

The mental condition, educated by experience, which accepts the ordinary phenomena of life and acts instinctively according to what is known as common sense, indicates an immediate acceptance of conditions long after the train of initial causes has been forgotten.

B. ASSOCIATION

Association short of the actual conditions, lends conviction as long as the essential elements are present.

C. JUDGMENT

An instinctive and immediate acceptance of visual effects for the sake of orientation, influenced by experience and association, awakens very little judgment. However, any intellectual analysis necessary for orientation, involves decision. Errors in judgment cause illusion. Even consciousness of the error does not completely overbalance the effect of illusion.

D. WILL

The will to believe depends upon the expected, or acceptable unexpected, sequences as developed in the suggestions of the program of the plot of the play, and our conviction through associational experience. We all have preconceived opinions and mental images and ordinarily will believe things that happen as we think they should, unless they are convincingly presented to the contrary.

E. INTEREST

Natural, professional, or acquired interests endow certain details in general visual presentation with special importance.

F. ABSTRACT APPEAL

The abstract appeal of music strikes something in our natures that is indefinable. The aesthetic appeal of the non-associational experience is often one of the greatest sources of emotional reaction. Something spiritual or metaphysical is superimposed on the physical stimulus.

V. PSYCHOLOGY OF VISION

The manner in which each of the qualities of light as distinguishable characteristics of sensation is influenced by these elements and helps to create a perception in view of them, is considered under the psychology of vision. Considering the involuntary interpretation of the effects of the qualities of light, the designer should attempt to use the particular aspect of each which in combination, contributes to the creation of a desired perception.

Inasmuch as concepts are formed by the simultaneous or sequential action of outside stimuli on all the senses, it is difficult to establish a simple set of suggestions which will define simply visual reactions to the qualities of light. Abstract visual compositions such as are demonstrated by the color organ are interpreted differently by almost every observer. However, as they take on associational form and color a certain unity of reaction results.

In the silent motion picture where photographic detail could be interpreted alike by all, and particularly when the actor appears on the screen, the unity of reaction is fairly well established. Titles narrow the diversity of perception still further. Sound and color bring the abstraction of light down to its ultimate limits until a true stereoscopic effect can be perfected. This example is used because the visual interpretation depends chiefly upon the production of light distribution to create definite perceptions. The screen in itself tells no story nor does it give any emotional reaction, except perhaps as we accept the convention as a photographic representation. The intimate personal appeal is not yet as complete as it has always been on the stage.

When light used on the stage no longer has to be accepted in its limited conventions due to the technical problems, or when it has its own accepted conventions, it will serve more definitely as a dramatic medium. When the designer is able to achieve the effect of abstract realism, and passes from that stage to selected dramatic expression, he can be sure that there will be unity of reaction to light. Sound, story, and the conditioning of the other senses influence the reception of lighting.

A. INTENSITY

The amount of visual stimulation that we are accustomed to receive under natural light is far beyond any limits that have been approached by artificial illumination. Due to the construction of the eye, relative intensities of artificial light often seem to have a greater range than natural light.

1. Experience leads us to accept any brightness or relative brightness that approaches natural effects. Glare often takes place under such lower intensities due to surrounding conditions.

2. Association with the effects of motivating sources: moonlight, sunlight, lamplight, etc. The problem of visibility as compared with naturalistic effect of motivating light.

3. Attention commanded by the relative illumination of essential features. Orientation due to general effect of illumination.

4. Expected illumination for realism. Unexpected for dramatic or exaggerated arbitrary effects.

5. Strong illumination where objects should be seen clearly. Dim where they should be imagined. Special interest demands that certain details be illuminated more than others.

6. High General illumination usually the symbol of comedy, a comfortable range. Low illumination or extreme brightness, symbols of tragedy.

B. COLOR

The psychology of color as a consideration of the mental reactions due to color alone has very hazy limits. The attractive power of color is great enough to be considered as a dominating factor over other influences that normally accompany it. It is possible, however, to vary these other influences to such an extent that each suggestion listed as a normal psychological reaction to color is obviously altered or untrue.

1. All hues, tints and shades of color as experienced in nature are connected with some object or customary action. Brightness of transmitted color is greater than brightness of reflected color with white light.

2. Associational attributes of all color effects. Naming of colors by the object which normally appears in that particular shade or tint of color. Confusion of terminology.

3. Normal coloring for familiar objects and situations. Exaggerated color for arbitrary and dramatic effects.

4. Expected or unexpected color composition.

5. Color Preference.

6. The Aesthetic Appeal of Color. Symbolism attached to color. Comedy—bright warm tints, or balanced colors. Tragedy—cool shades, or extremes in the warm zone.

C. FORM

Interpretation of pattern of light in intensity and color on the retina involves, perhaps, the most significant quality of light. It has a particular bearing on the psychological effects of color and of itself is the answer to all appeal of composition as we see it in pictures and drawings. In other words, the static pictorial effect depends greatly upon the form of light as it reaches the eye. Convention of light distribution in the theatre.

1. Experience in the effects of nature establishes a relationship between intensity and color in pattern.

2. The associational value of the form of an object or our relation to the objects and their relation to each other in the field of vision helps to establish the actuality of the scene.

3. The Conviction of Space Relationships. Contrasts.

4. Emphasis. Compels attention. Acting-area lighting.

5. Composition. Balance of lighting over the stage for pictorial effect.

6. Harmony of visual appeal due to the propriety and excellence of composition. Abstract patterns of light. Use of light to suggest movement and rhythm. Balance of distribution and color, average detail, for comedy. General mass or sharp detail for tragedy.

D. MOVEMENT

Movement is any change of intensity, color or form; the particular quality of light which cooperates with the arts of time—music and poetry—as they are found in the theatre. It thus forms a bond between the static and mobile arts—a common denominator which helps to make architecture, sculpture, painting, music and poetry live together as one dramatic expression. The ability to create a mobile atmosphere through the intensity, color, and form of light, as it relates to the static elements of a setting, costume, and make-up, and put them into harmony with the movement of the actor, makes them live as dramatic characters in the experience of the audience. It is possible to create a synchronous change of atmosphere to accompany every change of situation in the play.

1. The ever-changing effects of sunlight as precedent for changing light distribution. Subtleness of effect.

2. Association with life, vitality with changes.

3. Acceptance of change in lighting as a natural effect on the stage. Rapid changes cause distraction.

4. The convention of dimming house lights in expectancy of the scene. The compelling attraction of movement in light.

5. Changes tend to excite interest.

6. The unconscious effect of movement in the field of vision; change. Low intensity to high intensity. From depressing to pleasurable effect, and vice versa. Change from cool colors to warm colors gives more or less the same effect. Average movement consistent with comedy. Rapid change or slow movement consistent with tragedy.

123

APPENDIX III

SCHEDULE OF LAMPS USED IN
VARIOUS TYPES OF STANDARD STAGE LIGHTING EQUIPMENT

(NOTE: This list includes only the lamps most generally used. It does not include all lamps, nor does it include special equipment and the lamps used in it.)

I. SPOTLIGHTS

(a) PLANO-CONVEX - Burn Base Down to horizontal

5" Baby Medium Screw Base ...	250 W	G-30
	400 W	G-30
6" Standard Mogul Screw Base ...	500 W	G-40
	1000 W	G-40
	1500 W	G-40
8" Standard Mogul Screw Base ...	1500 W	G-40
	2000 W	G-48

(b) FRESNEL - Burn Base Down to horizontal

3" Bayonet Base ..	100 W	16½
	150 W	16½
6" Medium Prefocus Base	250 W	T-20
	500 W	T-20
	750 W	T-20
8" Mogul Prefocus Base	1000 W	G-40
	1500 W	G-40
10" Mogul Bipost Base	2000 W	G-48
14" Mogul Bipost Base	5000 W	G-64

(c) ELLIPSOIDAL REF. SPOT-Burn Base up to 45°

4½" Medium Prefocus Base ..	250 W	T-12
	500 W	T-12
6" Medium Prefocus Base	250 W	T-12
	500 W	T-12
	750 W	T-12
8" Medium Prefocus Base	250 W	T-12
	500 W	T-12
	750 W	T-12
8" Mogul Bipost Base	1000 W	T-24
	1500 W	T-24
	2000 W	T-30
12" Mogul Bipost Base	3000 W	T-32

II. PROJECTORS - Burn Base Down to Horizontal

10" Medium Prefocus Base	250 W	T-20
	500 W	T-20
16" Mogul Screw Base .	500 W	G-40
	1000 W	G-40
	1500 W	G-40
16" Mogul Prefocus Base	1000 W	G-40
	1500 W	G-40
16" Mogul Bipost Base .	2000 W	G-48

III. FLOODS

8" Medium Screw Base- any angle	100 W	A-21
Burn Base down to horizontal	250 W	G-30
	400 W	G-30
14" Mogul Screw Base . Burn any style	500 W	PS-40
18" Mogul Screw Base . Burn Base up to horizontal	750 W	PS-52
	1000 W	PS-52
	1500 W	PS-52
	2000 W	PS-52

IV. FOOTLIGHTS — Medium Screw Base

4" Reflector	25 W	A-19
	40 W	A-19
	60 W	A-19
	75 W	A-19
6" Reflector	100 W	A-20
	150 W	PS-25

V. BORDERLIGHTS — Medium Screw Base*

6" Reflector	100 W	A-21
	150 W	PS-25
6" Compartment ...... No reflector .... Glass Color Filters .	150 W	PAR-38 SP
	150 W	PAR-38 FL
	150 W	R-40 FL
	300 W	R-40 FL
	300 W	R-40 SP
8" Reflector	200 W	PS-30
	300 W	PS-30
12" *Mogul Screw Base.	300 W	PS-35
	500 W	PS-40

LAMP CODE (Number following initials equals diameter of bulb in eighth inches.)

A—Small wattage to 150	PAR—Parabolic reflector
G—Globe shaped	R—Reflector
PS Pear shaped	FL—Flood
T—Tubular	SP—Spot

APPENDIX IV

BEAM CANDLE-POWER TABLES FOR SPOTLIGHTS

(Approximate Amounts)

1. PLANO-CONVEX SPOTS

LAMP WATTAGE	LENS DIAM. & F. L.		MAXIMUM BEAM CANDLE POWER AT:		
			10°	30°	50°
250	4½ x 7½		7,000	2,000	1,000
400	5 x 9·		13,000	3,500	1,800
1000	6 x 10		35,000	10,000	5,000
1500	8 x 12		56,000	16,000	8,000

Hard Edge Beam:

(Note: Beam Spread Angle is taken where candle power is one-tenth maximum.)

2. FRESNEL SPOTLIGHTS

LAMP WATTAGE	LENS DIAM. & F. L.		MAXIMUM BEAM CANDLE POWER AT:			
			15°	25°		
100	3 x 2¼		4,000	2,500	40°	1,000
250	6 x 3 7/16		20,000	7,000	60°	3,000
500	6 x 3 7/16		60,000	14,000	60°	7,200
1000	8 x 4¾		110,000	45,000	40°	15,000
1500	8 x 4¾		180,000	75,000	40°	30,000
2000	10 x 5¾		250,000	110,000	40°	50,000
5000	14 x 8		700,000	220,000	40°	100,000

Soft Edge Beam:

(Note: Beam Spread Angle is taken where candle power is one-quarter maximum.)

3. ELLIPSOIDAL REFLECTOR SPOTS

LAMP WATTAGE	LENS DIAM. & F. L.	GATE DIAM.	BEAM SPREAD IN DEGREES	BEAM CANDLE-POWER	
				Minimum (at edge)	Maximum (at center)
250	2-4½ x 6½	3"	45°	800	8,000
500	2-4½ x 6½	3"	45°	2,000	20,000
500	2-6" x 9"	3"	32°	6,000	30,000
750	2-6" x 9"	3"	32°	8,500	50,000
500	8 x 10	3"	16°	13,000	100,000
750	8 x 10	3"	16°	18,000	150,000
1000	8 x 10	3¾"	22°	18,000	80,000
1500	8 x 10	3¾"	22°	30,000	130,000
2000	8 x 10	3¾"	22°	40,000	200,000
3000	12 x 20	4"	10°	200,000	650,000

Hard Edge Beam:

(Note: Beam can be made soft-edged by moving lens forward or back. Candle power at center does not change appreciably as gate is closed but the beam spread changes proportionally.)

* Step Lens

GENERAL NOTE: Voltage variation from rated amount, condition of lamp and reflectors, and general maintenance neglect may reduce the above beam candle powers up to 50%.

APPENDIX V.

STAGE: Width 50'-60', Depth 25'-30'   INSTRUMENT SCHEDULE FOR A MEDIUM STAGE   PROSCENIUM: Width 28'-30', Height 15'-18'

ITEM	NO. OF UNITS	TYPE OF UNIT	POSITION	USE	LAMP ORDERING NO.	LENS Diameter and Focal Length	REFLECTOR Shape Surface	MOUNTING	CONNECTING PROVISIONS PER UNIT OR PER SECTION
				ESSENTIAL FOR AVERAGE INTERIOR SETS					
1	6	Ellipsoidal Spotlight	False beam or Balcony Front	Front Acting Areas	750T12/9	Plane-Convex 8" x 10"	Ellipsoidal Alzak	Yoke, Pipe, and Twist Lock Connector	18" pigtail, 20 amp. Twist Lock Connector
2	6	Fresnel Spotlight	First Pipe	Rear Acting Areas	500T20/64	Fresnel	Spherical Alzak	Yoke, Pipe, and Clamp	18" Pigtail, 20 amp. Twist Lock
3	1 / 2	8'section / 4'sections Striplights	At front edge of stage apron	Footlights	150R/F			In Trough	4 18" Pigtails, 20 amp. Twist Locks at each end
4	2	8' sections Striplights	First Pipe	Blending of Acting Areas	150PAR/FL			End Studs, Arms, and Pipe Clamps	4 18" Pigtails, 20 amp. Twist Locks at each end
				IN ADDITION: ESSENTIAL FOR EXTERIOR SETS					
6	2 / 6	8' sections / 4' sections Striplights	At top of Cyclorama	Lighting the Cyclorama from above	300R/SP			End Studs, Arms, and Pipe Clamps	4 18"Pigtails, 20 amp. Twist Locks at each end
5	2 / 4	6' sections / 4 1/2' sections striplights	At foot of Cyclorama	Lighting the Cyclorama from below	150PAR/FL			End Studs, and Castered Base	3 18" Pigtails, 20 amp. Twist locks at each end
				FOR SPECIAL PURPOSES: HALF OF EACH ITEM ESSENTIAL					
7	4	Ellipsoidal Spotlights	Where Needed	Special Effects	500T12/9	2 Plane-Convex 6" x 9"	Ellipsoidal Alzak	Yoke, Pipe, and Clamp	18" Pigtail, 20 amp. Twist Lock
8	4	Ellipsoidal Spotlights	Where Needed	Special Effects	500T12/9	Stepped 4 1/2 x 3 1/2"	Ellipsoidal Alzak	Yoke, Pipe, and Clamp	18" Pigtail, 20 amp. Twist Lock
9	8	Fresnel Spotlights	Where Needed	Special Effects	500T20/64	Fresnel 6" x 3 1/2"	Spherical Alzak	Yoke, Pipe, and Clamp	18" Pigtail, 20 amp. Twist Lock
10	4	Fresnel Spotlights	In the Wings	Sunlight Moonlight	1M/G40/20	Fresnel 8" x 4 3/4"	Spherical Alzak	On castered Stand	18" Pigtail, 20 amp. Twist Lock
11	4	Ellipsoidal Floodlights	Where Needed	Backings Entrances	400G40/20		Ellipsoidal Etched Aluminum	Yoke, Pipe, and Clamp	18" Pigtail, 20 amp. Twist Lock
12	4	6' sections Striplights	Where Needed	Ground Rows Backings	150R/FL or 150R/Sp			End Studs	3 18" Pigtails, 20 amp. Twist locks at each end

For the FOOTLIGHTS: Use RED, GREEN and BLUE; for the BORDERLIGHTS use MAGENTA, CYAN BLUE and AMBER.
For the CYCLORAMA LIGHTS: Use DARK BLUE, LIGHT BLUE and AMBER overhead. Use RED, GREEN and BLUE in the Cyclorama footlights.

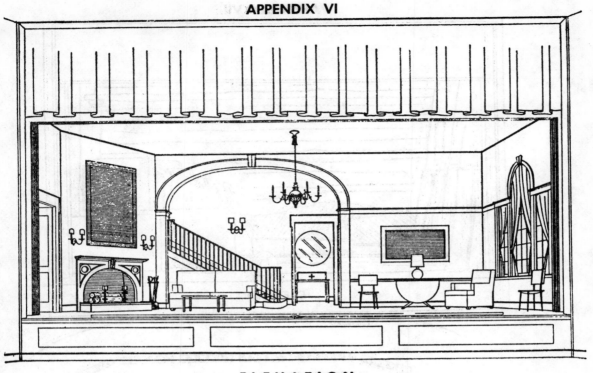

ELEVATION

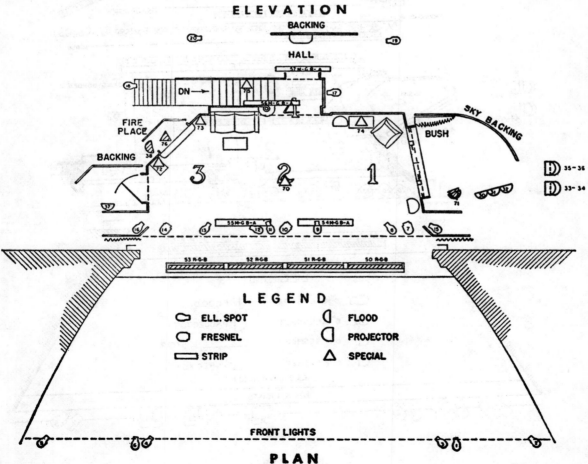

BACKING

HALL

FIRE
PLACE

BACKING

SKY BACKING

BUSH

3   2   1

LEGEND

�	ELL. SPOT		FLOOD
◯	FRESNEL		PROJECTOR
▭	STRIP	△	SPECIAL

FRONT LIGHTS

PLAN

APPENDIX VII

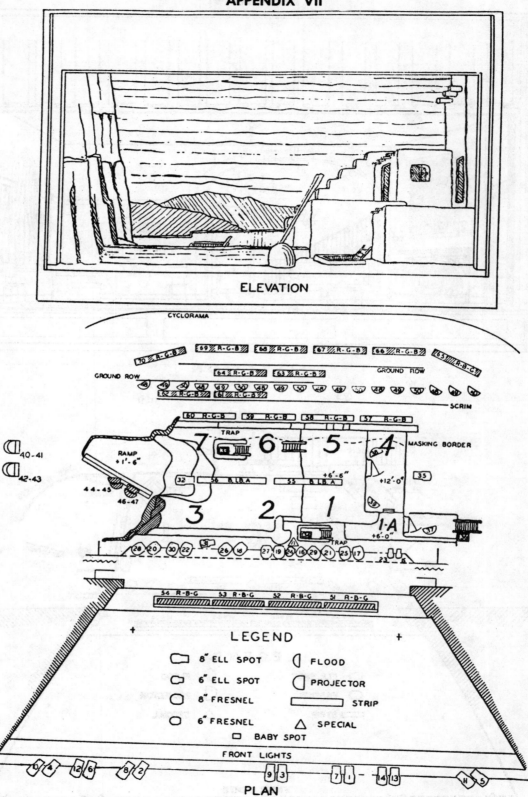

ELEVATION

PLAN

LEGEND

⬭ 8" ELL SPOT   ◖ FLOOD

⬭ 6" ELL SPOT   ◗ PROJECTOR

⬯ 8" FRESNEL   ▭ STRIP

○ 6" FRESNEL   △ SPECIAL

▢ BABY SPOT

FRONT LIGHTS

. . . HYPOTHETICAL INTERIOR

SCHEDULE OF EQUIPMENT

ITEM	TYPE OF INSTRUMENT	POSITION	USE	LAMP	TOTAL WATTS	DIM NO.	CABLE	ACCESSORIES	COLORS PER ACT I	II	III	NOTES
1-3	6" ELL. SPOT	CEIL. BEAM L	AREA 1,2,3 L	500 W T-12	1500	1,2,3	15'25'15'	YOKE & PIPE CLAMP	62		29	FRAME TO TOR. & TEAS.
4-6	"	" " R	" " R	"		4,5,6	15'25'15'	"	3		26	" " " "
7	6" FRES SPOT	1 PIPE L	TABLE L	500 W T-20	500	19	50'	"			58	SOFT EDGE
8	6" ELL. SPOT	"	ARCH L	500 W T-12	"	11	50'	"	62		29	FRAME TO STAIRS
9	"	"	AREA 4 L	"	"	7	40'	"	62		29	FRAME TO ARCH
10	6" FRES. SPOT	1 PIPE CENT.	TABLE R	500 W T-20	"	20	40'	"			54	SOFT EDGE
11	4½" ELL. SPOT	1 PIPE R	SOFA L	500 W T-12	"	9	40'	"	62		29	
12	6" ELL SPOT	"	DOOR R	"	"	22	40'	"	62		29	FRAME TO DOOR
13	"	"	ARCH R	"	"	12	30'	"	3		26	FRAME TO UPPER STAIRS
14	6" FRES SPOT	"	AREA 4 R	500 W T-20	"	8	30'	"	3		26	
15	6" ELL. SPOT	TOR L	SOFA FIRE	500 W T-12	"	21	60'	YOKE & ARM		57	60	FRAME TO SOFA STAIRS
16	"	TOR. R	SOFA R	"	"	10	25'	"	3	54	26	" " " "
17	"	20 PIPE L	STAIR L	"	1000	23	75'	YOKE 2'ARM P.CLAMP	62		29	FRAME TO STAIRS
18	"	20 PIPE R	STAIR R	"		23	50'	YOKE & PIPE CLAMP	3		26	" " " "
19	"	HALL R	HALL L	"	"	24	100'	8' STAND & YOKE	62		29	FRAME TO HALL ENT.
20	"	HALL L	HALL R	"		24	50'	"	3		26	" " " "
30-32	3-16" FLOODS	BACKING L	SKY BACK	500 W PS	1500	25	75'	10' STAND & ARMS	27			MULT. TOGETHER
33-34	2-16" PROJ	DN STAGE L	SUN	1500 W G-40	3000	26	2-100'	"	57			MULT AT BOARD
35-36	"	"	MOON	1000 W G-40	2000	26	2-100'	"		29-29		REPLUG
37	10" FLOOD	DOOR R	DOOR BACK	100 A-21	100	13	25'	BRACKET TO SET	1			LIGHT BACKING ONLY
38	"	FIREPLACE	FIRE FLOOD	400 W G-30	400	14	25'	BASE	57 67			VARIEGATED GELATINE
50 R 51 52 G 53 B	4-6' 12 LT STRIPS	FOOTLIGHT TROUGH	FOOTS	100 W A-21	1600 " "	28 29 30	25' 25' 25'	END STUD TRUNION	R G B			FEED THROUGH SECTION TO SECTION
54 M BG 55 A	2-6' 12 LT. STRIPS	2 PIPE	1 BORDER	150 W R40 FLOOD	1200 " "	31 32 33	25' 25' 25'	END STUD ARM & PIPE CLAMP	11 42 58			
56	1-6' 12 LT. STRIP	18 PIPE R	ARCH STRIP	150 W R-40	"	34	75'75'	"	11			
57	"	22 PIPE	HALL BACK.	FLOODS	" "	35 36	75'75' 75'75'	"	42 58			MULT AT BOARD
70	FIXTURE	10'H-7'U-C	CHAND.	6 W F	72	18	75'				58	
71	3-16" FLOODS	5'H-6'U-18'L	DIFFUSER	500 W PS40	1500	27	75'		26			MULT. AT STAND
72-73	WALL FIX.	AT FIRE PL	BRACKET	40 W A-19	160	17	4-30'	SHADE			C	MULT. AT FIREPLACE
74	TABLE LAMP	TABLE	LAMP	200 W PS30	200	16	75'	"			C	SHADE SHIELDED FRONT & TOP
75	WALL FIX.	STAIR WALL	BRACKET	40 W A-19	80	17	75'	"			58	
76	FIRE ROTOR	FIREPLACE	FIRE	2-250 W T20	500	15	50'	"			C	ROTOR & FIRE LOGS

CUE SHEET

ACT		DIM. BOARD	A on 37						B on 38					C on 39						D on 40						E													F			
	SCENE	1 1 L	2 1 L	3 2 L	4 1 R	5 2 R	6 3 R	7 4 L	8 4 R	9 SOFA L	10 SOFA R	11 ARCH L	12 ARCH R	13 DOOR B	14 FIRE FLOOD	15 FIRE	16 TABLE LAMP	17 BRACKETS	18 CHAND	19 TABLE L	20 TABLE R	21 SOFA FIRE	22 DOOR R	23 STAIR R	24 HALL L&R	25 SKY	26 SUN & MOON	27 DAYLIGHT	28 FOOT R	29 FOOT G	30 FOOT B	31 1 BOR. P	32 1 BOR. BG	33 1 BOR. A	34 ARCH P	35 ARCH GB	36 ARCH A	37 BOARD A	38 BOARD B	39 BOARD C	40 BOARD D
I	1	6	7	7	8	8	7	5	6	6	5	7	5	6							5	3	5	10	S8	10	4	5			3				6	10	10	10	10
CUE	OPEN																		NO CHANGE						UP & DOWN WITH CURTAIN																
II	1		5	5	5	5		5	5	5	7		6	5	4	46			8		8	5	3	3	4	M5			3		3			3		10	10	10	10
CUE	OPEN																		NO CHANGE						UP & DOWN WITH CURTAIN																
III	1	9	10	10	6	6	5	7	6	5	7	7	5	2	5	10	7	8	8	7	2	5	5	5	4	M10		6	5	3	3	2	6	3	2	6	5	7	10	10
CUE	OPEN		SLOW CHANGE										20 MIN. FROM RISE OF CURTAIN										DIM UP WITH CURTAIN																
READING	2								8				5								7	7	6	M3	3			5	4	5		4		6		6	8			7
CUE	HOLD (5 MIN. 2)		WARN "IT'S ALMOST DAY"										CUE: BUSINESS PULL CURTAINS, DIM IN 2 COUNTS																											
READING	3									9		5	7						3	8	8			MO			6	6	7		6	7		8	9					
CUE	HOLD (1 MIN ?)		WARN: CUE 3. COUNT						CUE: "PUT OUT LIGHTS" BUSINESS IN 3 STEPS (SWITCHES)																															
READING	4			⑤5	⑨5	⑤5	⑤5	③3	③4	⑦0	⓪0	⓪0	②	⑤	⑤4												②0	②0			⑨0			⑤0						
CUE	SLOW CHANGE 10 MIN (?) FINISH JUST BEFORE CURTAIN LINE REPLUG M TO S																																								
READING	5				8		10	7	9	7	7	0	6		5		0		7	10	10	S5	10			8	7	8		7	8		10	10		10				

DIM OUT AT CURTAIN

DESCRIPTION
ACT I MORNING
ACT II NIGHT — CHANDELIER & FIRE
ACT III DAWN — FIXTURE LIGHT TO SUNRISE

PORTABLE SWITCHBOARDS RESISTANCE TYPE DIMMERS
CIR. 1-6 500W   BOARD A   CIR. 19-24 500W   BOARD D
" 7-12 "   " B   " 25-36 1500-3000W   " E
" 13-18 500-1000W   " C   " 37-40 4000W   " F

DIMMER READINGS
0 = OUT   10 = FULL

REALISTIC EXTERIOR

SCHEDULE OF EQUIPMENT

GROUP	ITEM	TYPE OF INSTRUMENT	POSITION	USE	LAMP	TOTAL WATTS	DIM NO	ACCESSORIES	COLORS	NOTES
SPOTS	1	8"ELL SPOT	CEIL BEAM L	AREA 1LW	750W T-12	750	3	YOKE & PIPE CL	17	FRAME TO TEASER & AREA
	2	" " "	" " R	" 1R&1ARW	"	"	1	" " "	57	
	3	" " "	" " L	" 2LW	"	"	5	" " "	17	" " " " "
	4	" " "	" " R	" 2RW	"	"	1	" " "	57	" " " " "
	5	" " "	" " L	" 3LW	"	"	5	" " "	17	" " " " "
	6	" " "	" " R	" 3RW	500W T-12	500	1	" " "	57	" " " " "
	7	" " "	" " L	" 1LC	"	"	4	" " "	29	" " " " "
	8	" " "	" " R	" 1R&1ARC	"	"	2	" " "	CL	" " " " "
	9	" " "	" " L	" 2LC	"	"	6	" " "	29	" " " " "
	10	" " "	" " R	" 2RC	"	"	2	" " "	CL	" " " " "
	11	" " "	" " L	" 3LC	750W T-12	750	6	" " "	29	" " " " "
	12	" " "	" " R	" 3RC	500W T-12	500	2	" " "	CL	" " " " "
	13	" " "	" " L	" 1ALW	"	"	5	" " "	17	" " " " "
	14	" " "	" " L	" 1ALC	"	"	6	" " "	29	" " " " "
	15	6"ELL SPOT	2 PIPE L	" 4LW	500W T-12	500	11	" " "	17	FRAME TO AREA OFF SCRIM
	16	6"FRES. SPOT	2 PIPE LC	" 4RW	500 W T-20	"	7	" " "	57	MAT TO AREA OFF SCRIM
	17	8" " "	1 PIPE L	" 5L W	1000W G-40	1000	11	" " "	17	
	18	" " "	" R	" 5 R W	"	"	7	" " "	57	
	19	" " "	" LC	" 6 L W	"	"	12	" " "	17	
	20	" " "	" R	" 6RW	"	"	8	" " "	57	
	21	" " "	" L	" 7 L W	"	"	12	" " "	17	
	22	" " "	" R	" 7 R W	"	"	8	" " "	57	
	23	6"ELL SPOT	2 PIPE L	" 4LC	500 T-12	500	13	" " "	29	
	24	6"FRES. SPOT	" LC	" 4RC	500 T-20		9	" " "	CL	
	25	8" " "	1 PIPE L	" 5LC	1000 WG-40	1000	13	" " "	29	
	26	" " "	" R	" 5RC	"	"	9	" " "	CL	
	27	" " "	" L	" 6LC	"	"	14	" " "	29	
	28	" " "	" R	" 6RC	"	"	10	" " "	CL	
	29	" " "	" L	" 7LC	"	"	14	" " "	29	
	30	" " "	" R	" 7RC	"	"	10	" " "	CL	
	31	6"ELL. SPOT	2 PIPE R	D.S TRAP SP.	500W T-12	500	15	LONG ARM Y & PC	CL	MAT TO AREA
	32	" " "	3 PIPE R	DOOR SP.	750W T-12	750	16	YOKE & P.C.	CL	MAT TO DOOR
	33	5"PL. CON.SPOT	TRAP U.R	UR.TRAP SP	400W G-30	400	17	YOKE & STAND	CL	MAT TO AREA
	34	" "	" D.L.	D.L.	"	"	17	" " "	CL	
	35	6"ELL SPOT	U L+6'6"	ENT SP	500W T-12	500	18	" " "	CL	
	36	5"PL CON SPOT	DL+6'	ENT SP	400 W G-30	400	17	" " "	CL	
FLOODS	37	10"ELL. FL.	DL +6'	DOOR BACK	250WG-30	250	19	8' STAND	26+1	LT. BACKING
	38	" " "	U.L.+6'6"	ROOM	"	"	20		26+1	" "
	39	" " "	L.+6'6"	"	"	"	20		26+1	" "
	40	16" BEAM PR.	R+50'	SUN AREA 4	1500 W G 40	1500	46	Y& P.C. LADDER	54	
	41	" " "	R+42'	" " 5&1	"	"	46	"	54	
	42	" " "	R+30'	" " 6&2	"	"	47	"	54	
	43	" " "	R+24'	" " 7&3	"	"	47	"	54	
	44	14"ELL FL.	R+14'	DAY FLOOD	500 PS 40	500	21	"	26+1	" "
	45	" " "	R+12'	"	"	"	21	"	26+1	" "
	46	" " "	R+10'	"	"	"	21	"	26+1	" "
	47	" " "	R+8'	"	"	"	21	"	26+1	
	48	6 14"ELL. FLS	5 PIPE	CYC OVER.	"	3000	37	YOKE & PIPE CL	57	LT. UPPER CYC
	49	" " "	"	"	"	"	38	"	48	
	50	" " "	"	"	"	"	39	"	39	
STRIPS	51 R	4 6' 12 LT. STRIPS	FOOTLIGHT TROUGH	FOOTS	100W A-21	1600	22	END STUD TRUNION	R. GLASS	FEED THROUGH SECTION TO SECTION
	52 G					"	23		G. "	
	54 B					"	24		B. "	
	55A	2 8' 12 LT. STRIPS	3RD. PIPE +28'	2ND BORDERS	200 PS-36	1600	25	END STUD ARM & PIPE CLAMP	A. GLASS	"
	56B					"	26		B. "	
							27			
	57 R	4 6' 12 LT. STRIPS	4TH. PIPE +34'	GAUZE TOP	150W PAR-38 SPOT	2400	34	SPREAD ROUNDEL	R "	"
	58 G						35		G "	
	60 B					"	36		B "	
	61 R	2 6' 12 LT. STRIPS	U.R. FLOOR GROUND ROW	GROUND ROW FOOTS	150W R-40 FLOOD	1200	28	END STUD & TRUNION SPREAD ROUNDEL	R "	"
	62 G					"	29		G "	
	63 B					"	30			
	64					"	31		B "	
						"	32			
						"	33			
	65 R	3 6' 12 LT. STRIPS	U.S. FLOOR CYC L.	CYC FOOTS	300W R-40 SPOT	3600	40	"	R "	"
	66 G					"	41		G "	
	67 B					"	42		B "	
	68 R	"	U.S. FLOOR CYC R	"	"	"	43	"	R "	"
	69 G					"	44		G "	
	70 B					"	45		B "	
	71	EFFECT MACH	2ND. PIPE	SCENE PROJECT.	5000W T-32	5000	48		AUTO SLIDE CHANGER	

BIBLIOGRAPHY

INTRODUCTION

Bowman, Wayne, MODERN THEATRE LIGHTING, Harper and Brothers, New York.
Bricker, Herschel L., OUR THEATRE TODAY, Samuel French, New York.
Fuchs, Theodore, STAGE LIGHTING, Little, Brown, and Company, Boston.
Jones, Robert Edmund, and Kenneth Macgowan, CONTINENTAL STAGECRAFT,
    Harcourt, Brace, New York.
McCandless, Stanley, A METHOD OF LIGHTING THE STAGE, Theatre Arts Books,
    New York.
Parker, W. Oren, and Harvey K. Smith, SCENE DESIGN AND STAGE LIGHTING,
    Holt, Rinehart and Winston, New York.

Chapter 1. LIGHT SOURCES

Fuchs, STAGE LIGHTING
Parker and Smith, SCENE DESIGN AND STAGE LIGHTING
Catalogs of the Lamp Manufacturing Companies

Chapter 2. INSTRUMENTS

Bowman, MODERN THEATRE LIGHTING
Dull, and Williams, MODERN PHYSICS,
    Holt, Rinehart and Winston, New York
Fuchs, STAGE LIGHTING
Kook, IMAGES IN LIGHT FOR THE LIVING THEATRE,
    Century Lighting, Inc., New York.
McCandless, A METHOD OF LIGHTING THE STAGE
Parker and Smith, SCENE DESIGN AND STAGE LIGHTING
Selden, Samuel, and Hunton D. Sellman, STAGE SCENERY AND LIGHTING,
    Appleton-Century-Crafts, New York.
Catalogs of the Stage Lighting Instruments Companies.

Chapter 3. CONTROL

Bowman, MODERN THEATRE LIGHTING
Dull, Metcalfe and Williams, MODERN PHYSICS
Fuchs, STAGE LIGHTING
Navy Training Course, BASIC ELECTRICITY, United States Government Printing Office,
    Washington
Parker and Smith, SCENE DESIGN AND STAGE LIGHTING
Selden and Sellman, STAGE SCENERY AND LIGHTING
Catalogs of the Lighting Control Equipment Companies

Chapter 4. LAYOUT

Fuchs, STAGE LIGHTING
McCandless, A METHOD OF LIGHTING THE STAGE
Parker and Smith, SCENE DESIGN AND STAGE LIGHTING

Chapter 5. FUNCTIONS OF STAGE LIGHTING

Bricker, OUR THEATRE TODAY
McCandless, A METHOD OF LIGHTING THE STAGE
McCandless, LIGHTING FOR THE AUDIENCE,
    Stanley McCandless
    253 Lawrence Street, New Haven, Conn.
Parker and Smith, SCENE DESIGN AND STAGE LIGHTING

Chapter 6. QUALITIES OF LIGHT

Bowman, MODERN THEATRE LIGHTING
Evans, AN INTRODUCTION TO COLOR, John Wiley and Sons, New York
Parker and Smith, SCENE DESIGN AND STAGE LIGHTING
Williams, THE TECHNIQUE OF STAGE LIGHTING, Pitman and Sons, London

Chapter 7. TECHNICAL ELEMENTS

General Electric Company, ILLUMINATION DESIGN DATA, General Electric Company,
    Nela Park, Cleveland
Illuminating Engineering Society, IES LIGHTING HANDBOOK,
    Illuminating Engineering Society, New York

Chapter 8. PROCEDURE

Bowman, MODERN THEATRE LIGHTING
Bricker, OUR THEATRE TODAY
Fuchs, STAGE LIGHTING
Parker and Smith, SCENE DESIGN AND STAGE LIGHTING
Rubin, Joel E., and Leland H. Watson, THEATRICAL LIGHTING PRACTICE,
    Theatre Art Books, New York

Appendix I. HISTORY

Fuchs, STAGE LIGHTING
Hartnoll, Phyllis, Ed., THE OXFORD COMPANION TO THE THEATRE,
    Oxford University Press, New York

Appendix II. PSYCHOLOGY

Fuchs, STAGE LIGHTING

INDEX